FUNDAMENTAL PHONICS

By
Renee Cummings
and
Meish Goldish

Cover Artist
Mia Tavonatti

Inside Illustrations by
Tim Foley

Publisher
Instructional Fair • TS Denison
Grand Rapids, Michigan 49544

Permission to Reproduce

About the Book

The *"Fun"damental Phonics* series was developed to incorporate language fun into phonics learning. The extensive use of poetry throughout the series is based on the premise that rhyme is one of the best tools to help students find patterns as they learn new sounds and words.

About the Authors

Renee Cummings brings 18 years of classroom experience to the books she has authored for teachers and children. Her other titles for Ideal • Instructional Fair include *Literature-Based Reading* and *Reading Comprehension*. Renee lives in Hood River, Oregon, with her husband, who is currently the town's mayor.

Meish Goldish has written more than 30 books for children, in a range that includes fiction, nonfiction, biography, and several poetry anthologies. His delightful phonics poems, found throughout this series, are his first works for Instructional Fair. Meish lives in Teaneck, New Jersey.

Credits

Authors: Renee Cummings and Meish Goldish
Cover Artist: Mia Tavonatti
Inside Illustrations: Tim Foley
Project Director/Editor: Kathryn Wheeler
Editors: Sharon Kirkwood, Wendy Roh Jenks
Page Design: Pat Geasler

Standard Book Number: 1-56822-857-0
"Fun"damental Phonics—Grade 3
Copyright © 1999 Ideal • Instructional Fair Publishing Group
a division of Tribune Education
2400 Turner Avenue NW
Grand Rapids, Michigan 49544

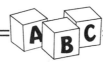

Table of Contents

Introduction 4–5

Blends

Brush Up /br/, /cr/ 6
Is This a Dream? /dr/ 7
My Friend Fred /fr/, /gr/ 8
Let's Pretend /pr/ 9
Traveling Along /tr/ 10
Slippery Blasts /bl/, /sl/ 11
Cleaning Up /cl/, /gl/ 12
Flies and Plums /fl/, /pl/ 13
Keep in Step /sk/, /st/ 14
Spinning Along /sm/, /sp/ 15
Scarecrows and Snails /sn/,
    /sc/ 16
Swirl and Twirl /sw/, /tw/ 17
Screeching Owl /scr/ 18
Splashing Fish /spl/ 19
Spring Has Sprung /spr/ 20
Squirrel Square /squ/ 21
Stretch Some String /str/ 22
Thread the Blends /thr/ 23

Digraphs

Choose Your Cake /ch/ 24
Share a Wish /sh/ 25
These Teeth /th/ 26
Whisper /wh/ 27
Phone an Elephant /ph/ 28
Enough! /gh/ 29

Silent and Variant Consonants

On the Knoll /kn/ 30
What Did I Write? /wr/ 31
Such a Sight! /gh/ 32
Gnats and Gnus /gn/ 33
Little Lamb /mb/ 34
Pitch and Catch /tch/ 35
Nice and Cozy /hard and
    soft c/ 36
On Stage /hard and soft g/ 37
On the Loose /hard s/ 38
What Rose Chose /soft s/ 39

Vowel Digraphs

Applause, Please /au/ 40
Mouse Law /aw/ 41
After Breakfast /ea/ 42
Eight Reindeer ei/ 43
Have a Piece /ie/ 44
Coast to Coast /oa/ 45

Diphthongs and Other Vowel Sounds

Loud Cloud /ou/ 46
Boil and Broil /oi/ 47
Enjoy! /oy/ 48
Unknown /ow/ 49
Take a Bow /ow/ 50
A Few of the Crew /ew/ 51

R-Controlled Vowels

My Special Jar /ar/ 52
In a Lion's Lair /air/ 53
Do You Dare? /are/ 54
Observe /er/ 55
Hear, Hear! /ear/ 56
Whirl Around /ir/ 57
Picture This /ure/ 58

Compound Words

An Underwater Adventure 59
Make the Connection 60
Campground Compounds 61
Baseball Fan 62
Link Up the Words 63
Till the Ground 64

Contractions

Put It Together /not/ 65
Contract It! /not/ 66
Would You Like To Skate?
    /have/, /would/ 67

You're Where? /are/, /am/ 68
What Will You Be? /will/ 69
What's That? /is/ 70

Prefixes

Unlike Others /un/ 71
Repeat It! /re/ 72
Impossible! /in/,/im/, /ir/ 73
Don't Disappear! /dis/ 74

Suffixes

Follow the Signs /s/ 75
Flashes and Crashes /es/ 76
Picked and Packed /ed/ 77
Spring Cleaning /ing/ 78
Read Silently, Please! /ly/ 79
Be a Word Inventor! /er/, /or/80
Are You Able? /able/ 81

Root Words

Get to the Root 82
Divide at the Root.................. 83

Homophones

Pair of Pears 84
That Makes Sense 85
Sail For Sale.......................... 86
Hoarse Horse 87
The Guest Guessed 88
One Lead to Another 89
I Read in Bed 90
An Ant and His Aunt 91
The Hair of a Hare 92
Homing in on Homophones 93

Activities

On the Move Game 94–98
Shape Up! Game 99–104
Letter/Sound Cards 105–106

Answer Key 107–128

IF87103 "Fun"damental Phonics

Introduction

"Fun"damental Phonics is designed to engage students actively in language play as they listen to and recognize sounds. The poems, games, and worksheet activities will help students understand the relationship between letters and sounds. Elements of language acquisition include listening, speaking, reading, and writing. Teachers can informally assess learning while introducing, practicing, and reviewing blends; digraphs; silent and variant consonants; diphthongs; r-controlled vowels; compound words; contractions; prefixes and suffixes; and homophones.

The sounds covered in this book are divided into groups so that you may introduce your students to each concept in turn. Language elements such as contractions, compound words, and homophones are included so that students may extend their understanding of how words and sounds are divided into units. When working with the classifications in this book, remember that some sounds, particularly vowel sounds, are classified differently by various linguists. Also keep in mind that in the United States, regional pronunciations of some of these sounds will vary.

All of the worksheets encourage active use of words within the context of poems, riddles, sentences, and stories. At the end of the book are games which will reinforce phonics learning with enjoyable, whole-class participation.

Poetry Presentation

In order to introduce a sound or phonics concept, poems and stories from the worksheets can be read aloud to your students. Depending on the methodology in use, more difficult words from the poem or story can be presented individually or grouped into phrases.

Ask students to listen as you read the poem or story. Invite interaction with the sound being introduced by asking questions such as, "What is the same about the words *princess* and *pretty*?" "Yes, they both begin with *pr*. And *pr* makes the /pr/ sound." Or point to a word in the poem and offer information such as,

"This word is *pear*. Can you name another word with the same sound but a different meaning?"

Some of the worksheets include creative writing exercises, such as composing short, rhyming poems or riddles. You can also organize your class to work on these and similar assignments as a whole or in teams. Have your students alter the worksheet poems by substituting new words. Ask students to brainstorm poetry lines that feature new rhymes. This will help strengthen their recognition of phonograms.

Sound Presentation

Many times, students will have trouble understanding the connection between sounds, letters, and words. Presenting sounds in rhymes and alliteration is one of the most effective ways to help students make these connections. Another effective tool is to have students relate sounds to words, and then use the words in context. The worksheets in this book offer that sequence to help students remember and gain confidence with new sounds.

When presenting a new sound by itself to students, try this sequence:

- Introduce the sound orally.

- Read the related poem/story or have students brainstorm words which employ the sound. Collect suggestions for a class Word Bank.

- Talk about how the sound is made: the shape of the mouth, the placement of the tongue, etc.

School-to-Home Connection

To keep parents/guardians informed of progress in phonics learning, it would be helpful to send home the worksheet of the week.

Attach the worksheet or other materials to a weekly newsletter explaining activities taking place in the classroom. This reinforces instruction about the featured sound or phonics concept. Ask for home involvement in sharing a featured poem, talking about a related story, or creating riddles based on concepts such as homophones.

On a designated day of the week, students could bring an object from home that contains the featured sound. These objects can be used during group phonics time to facilitate discussion.

Another idea would be to ask the student to find an item small enough to fit in a lunch bag. Have him/her work at home to write three clues that describe the object. Have each student present his or her clues to the class to see if the class can guess the mystery object.

Writing

As your third-graders become more confident with writing, writing exercises can be used to reinforce weekly phonics study. The emphasis on poetry, riddles, and stories in this book should help to make study and related writing more enjoyable. Encourage students to create their own poetry and stories, riddles, and even nonsense rhymes.

Continue to be aware of high frequency words, which foster fluency. Using these words to create word walls or dictionaries in wall or book format will help students with awareness of these connecting words, and increase fluency as they move past decoding and toward phonemic mastery.

IF87103 "Fun"damental Phonics

Name _____

Brush Up

Read the poems. Draw a line under the words that begin with the blend **br** or **cr**.

Brown bread
For breakfast
Brought to my room!
Breakfast crumbs need brushing up
Bring me the broom!

Crackers and cream
With cranberry crumble.
What a crazy lunch!
But I won't grumble,
Cry or mumble,
Instead I'll crunch, crunch, crunch!

Use the poems as Word Banks. Find the **br** or **cr** word to complete each rhyme.

1. Why such a frown?
   Don't you like the color _____ ?

2. He treated the team
   To cake and ice _____ .

3. The dog came rushing
   For its weekly _____ .

4. Threads fell from the loom.
   Sweep them up with the
   _____ .

5. Let's eat carrots for lunch!
   Then we can munch and _____ .

6. For all the hungry snackers,
   We have some saltine _____ .

7. We have food that we bought
   And the pies our friend
   _____ .

8. Geese like to be fed
   Crumbs of whole-wheat _____ .

9. Our new vacuum hums
   As it picks up the _____ .

10. There's a feast for the king!
    What may we _____ ?

IF87103 "Fun"damental Phonics

Name _____

Is This a Dream?

Write the blend **dr** on the lines to complete the words in the poem. Read the poem.

A _____ agon is _____inking
From the _____ipping _____ain.
Now it's _____agging
My _____esser _____awer!
It's _____umming my _____um,
It's _____ying a _____ess—
Oh, dear! I'm _____eaming some more!

Read the sentences. Use the poem as a Word Bank. Find the **dr** word to complete each sentence.

1. Betsy likes _____ the dishes every night.

2. Please see if the _____ is clogged.

3. Keisha bought a new _____ to wear to the birthday party.

4. We knew the parade was starting when we heard the _____ of the big drum.

5. Ahmed puts all of his awards on the _____ in his bedroom.

6. Cleo fell asleep under a tree, _____ about winning a skating medal.

7. They watched the squirrels _____ water from the birdbath.

8. Mom found her scissors in the silverware _____ .

9. The wet puppy ran across the kitchen, _____ water all over the floor!

10. Everyone laughed when they saw the puppy _____ Dad's robe.

7

IF87103 *"Fun"damental Phonics*

Name _____

My Friend Fred

Read the poems. Circle the words that begin with the blend **fr** or **gr**.

My friend Fred
Eats fresh fruit
And French fries,
While Fred's frog
Eats fresh flies!

Grab a bunch of green grapes,
The greatest snack around!
But *never* grab the green grass
Growing in the ground!

Use the poems to find the missing **fr** and **gr** words and write them in the puzzle.

Across:

1. Please ____ the keys off the table.

2. Bananas are good in a _____ salad.

5. Mike's best _____ is Joe.

7. Our team is the ____ of any team!

8. Mom _____ the chicken
   for the picnic.

Down:

1. The lack of rain has made the
   _____ very hard.

3. It's fun to skate outdoors in the
   ____ air.

4. Do you like seedless ____ ?

6. That sunflower is ____ taller
   than the fence!

IF87103 *"Fun"damental Phonics*

Name _____

Let's Pretend

Write the blend **pr** on the lines to complete the words in the poem. Read the poem.

Let's _____etend
We're _____ince and _____incess,
Very _____oud and _____etty.
People will _____aise us,
_____esent us with _____izes
As we _____otect our city!

Use the poem as a Word Bank. Use the **pr** words to complete the story.

     Priscilla and her friend Pruit like to _____ they are explorers or knights. Today, they decide to be rulers of a country. Priscilla says that she is a _____ and Pruit will be her brother, the _____ . They use old coats as their robes. They cut crowns out of cardboard. Walking around the yard with their heads held high, they look very _____ . Suddenly, Pruit jumps in front of Priscilla, pretending to _____ her from a fire-breathing dragon! Priscilla hurries over to the rosebush to pick a _____ , red rose for him. Then, they hear applause and someone shouting, "Hooray!" They turn and see their friend Beth. Priscilla and Pruit bow to her. Beth says, "You two should get _____ for your great acting!"

Write a poem about someone you like to pretend to be.

_____

_____

_____

_____

9

Traveling Along

Name _____

Write the blend **tr** on the lines to complete the words in the poem. Read the poem.

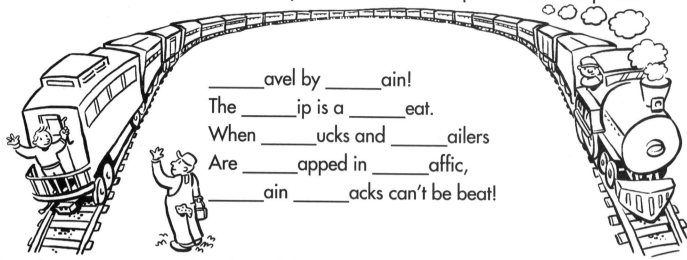

_____avel by _____ain!
The _____ip is a _____eat.
When _____ucks and _____ailers
Are _____apped in _____affic,
_____ain _____acks can't be beat!

Use the poem as a Word Bank. Find the **tr** word to complete each rhyme.

1. Long ago, on roads of <u>gravel</u>, people found it hard to _____ .

2. Because of the <u>rain</u>, we might miss the _____ !

3. Please take a <u>seat</u> so I can serve you a _____ .

4. As the kitten <u>napped</u>, he dreamed he was _____ .

5. The hockey players put sticks and <u>pucks</u> onto the waiting _____ .

6. The crew fixed the <u>cracks</u> along the railroad _____ .

Write a rhyme about a train.

_____

_____

_____

_____

IF87103 "Fun"damental Phonics

Name _____

Slippery Blasts

Read the poems. Draw a line under the words that begin with the blend **bl** or **sl**.

Blizzard blowing
On our block!
Blow! Blow!
Blankets of snow,
Blasts of snow!

Never sleep on a sled!
Never sleep on a sled!
You'll slip and slide,
It's a slippery ride!
No, never sleep on a sled!

Read the clues. Use the poem to find the missing **bl** and **sl** words and write them in the puzzle.

Across:

3. Listen to the wind _____ !

5. We have new _____ on our beds.

6. Let's go to the playground and play on the _____.

7. Don't _____ on the wet floor!

8. The icy roads are _____ .

Down:

1. We live one _____ from school.

2. School was let out early because of the big _____ .

3. I felt _____ of cold air whenever someone opened the door.

6. It is fun to _____ out in a tent.

7. Max likes to _____ down the snowy hills.

_____ _____ _____

IF87103 *"Fun"damental Phonics*

Name _____

Cleaning Up

Write the blend **cl** on the lines to complete the words in the poem. Read the poem.

_____imb up

And _____ean these _____ouds!

We can't see up here.

Take a _____oth

And _____ean up _____ose

Until each _____oud is _____ear!

Draw a line under words that begin with the blend **gl**. Read the poem

Gloves can glide
Over glass,
It's true,
Unless the glass
Has globs
Of glue!

Use the poems as Word Banks. Find the correct **cl** or **gl** word to solve each riddle.

1. These float in the sky. _____

2. These fit on your hands. _____

3. This sticks things together. _____

4. This is used to make clothing. _____

5. This is clear and can break. _____

6. This is what you do on ice skates. _____

7. This is the opposite of "far away." _____

12

Name _____

Flies and Plums

Read the poems. Draw a line under the words that begin with the blend **fl** or **pl**.

The fly flew to the flower,
The fly flew to the floor.
The fly flipped,
The fly flopped,
The fly flew out the door!

Please place those plump plums
On my paper plate.
I plan to eat plenty!
Place one, place two,
Plus three, plus four,
Until my plate holds twenty!

Use the poems as Word Banks. Find the missing **fl** or **pl** words that will rhyme with the underlined words and make sense. Write the words on the lines.

1. I'm sure <u>twenty</u> cakes will be _____ for the bake sale.

2. Martha wished she <u>knew</u> where the geese _____ .

3. When we opened the <u>door</u>, we found crumbs on the _____ .

4. Mom found just the right _____ to store the old <u>lace</u>.

5. Please don't <u>fuss</u>—we invited <u>Russ</u> _____ <u>Gus</u>!

6. <u>Nate</u> filled his _____ with chicken and salad.

7. Oh, _____ ! Use a tissue when you <u>sneeze</u>!

8. No matter how hard you <u>try</u>, you are not a bird; you cannot _____ .

9. Mom always <u>hums</u> when she is picking ripe _____ .

10. A bright yellow _____ grew by the <u>tower</u>.

11. Their holiday _____ was to get a <u>tan</u>.

IF87103 *"Fun"damental Phonics*

Name _____

Keep in Step

Read the poems. Draw a line under the words that begin with the blend **sk** or **st**.

To ski well
Takes special skills,
To skip and skate
And skid down hills.

Stop! Don't step!
Stay! Stand still!
Stop! Don't stir!
Stay! Steer clear!

Use the poems as Word Banks. Find the missing **sk** or **st** words to finish the puzzle.

Across:

1. Our cousins will _____ with us for a week.

3. I wish they would _____ playing the same song over and over!

5. It takes special _____ to ski well.

7. Don't _____ in the wet cement.

8. Max went to the mountains to learn how to _____ .

Down:

1. She will _____ gym because of her broken ankle.

2. Stand _____ and the bee will go away.

4. They went to the frozen pond to _____ .

6. Can you _____ a bumper car?

7. This thick batter is hard to _____ .

8. Sometimes bikes _____ on gravel roads.

14

Name _____

Spinning Along

Read the poems. Draw a line under the words that begin with the blend **sm** or **sp**.

Smell the soup.
Smack your lips.
Small smile,
Big smile,
Smooth soup in smug sips!

Without a single spatter,
I can spin spaghetti on my spoon.
Oops! A big spaghetti spill!
I guess I spoke too soon!

Use the poems as Word Banks. Find the correct **sm** or **sp** word in the poems to answer each riddle.

1. This goes with meatballs. _____
2. This is like a grin. _____
3. This is how a spider makes a web. _____
4. This is the opposite of "big." _____
5. This is the past tense of "speak." _____
6. This is what happens when milk is knocked over. _____
7. This is the opposite of "rough." _____
8. This goes with a knife and fork. _____

Write a tongue twister about spaghetti.

_____
_____
_____
_____

IF87103 *"Fun"damental Phonics*

Name _____

Scarecrows and Snails

Read the poems. Draw a line under the words that begin with the blend **sc** or **sn**.

The scarecrow
Has a scary scarf
To scare the crows away.
Scoot! Scat!
Scatter, crows!
Scoot and stay away!

Snake and Snail
Sniffed the snow,
Which muffled their snuffle attack.
Snake sneezed!
Snail sneezed!
Snow was on their backs!

Use the poems as Word Banks. Find the missing **sc** or **sn** word that rhymes with each underlined word and makes sense. Write it on the line.

1. Spot said "arf" as he ran off with my _____ .

2. The quiet quail watched the slow _____ .

3. A glass can shatter and pieces can _____ .

4. The puppy _____ the birthday gift.

5. At the end of the row stood a tattered _____ .

6. The fire's sudden flare gave us all a _____ .

7. Have you ever seen _____ drift and blow ?

8. The noise was _____ ; it frightened Larry.

9. A small _____ slithered to the lake.

10. Bob wheezed and _____ .

11. "_____ !" said Mrs. Jones to the big black cat.

IF87103 *"Fun"damental Phonics*

consonant blends: /sw/, /tw/

Name _____

Swirl and Twirl

Write the blend **sw** on the lines to complete the words in the poem. Read the poem.

A _____imming _____an
Is _____ift and _____eet,
So _____eet it _____eeps me
Off my feet!

Use the poem as a Word Bank. Find the **sw** word to complete each sentence.

1. An orange tastes _____ .
2. I like to go _____ in the lake on hot days.
3. Dan _____ the back porch with a broom.
4. A white _____ floated on the pond.
5. My bike is _____ on the new pavement.

Write the blend **tw** on the lines to complete the words in the poem. Read the poem.

_____ ist and _____irl!
_____ice is plenty!
Wait—_____ist _____elve times
Then _____irl _____enty!

Use the poem for a Word Bank. Write each missing **tw** word in the puzzle.

Across:

1. If thirteen girls and seven boys join the team, we will have ____ players.
2. There are _____ as many pears as apples.
3. Twilla can _____ a baton.

Down:

1. You have to _____ the lid to open the bottle.
2. There are _____ geese: six white and six brown.

© Instructional Fair • TS Denison

17

IF87103 *"Fun"damental Phonics*

Name _____

Screeching Owl

Write the blend **scr** on the lines to complete the words in the poem. Read the poem.

A _____ eeching owl

_____atches on my _____een,

_____aping for the food _____aps

It has seen.

Use the poem as a Word Bank. Find the correct **scr** word to answer each clue.

1. This is what the screeching owl scratches. _____

2. The screeching owl scratches the screen to get these. _____

3. This is the sound the owl makes while scratching the screen. _____

4. The screeching owl is doing this to get food scraps. _____

5. This is what the screeching owl does to the screen. _____

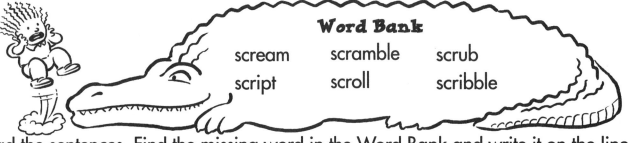

Word Bank

scream	scramble	scrub
script	scroll	scribble

Read the sentences. Find the missing word in the Word Bank and write it on the line.

1. Bob wants to _____ some eggs for breakfast.

2. Mr. Hernandez unrolled the _____ to read the names of the top students.

3. Please write neatly; don't _____ !

4. We had to use a brush to _____ the stain off the floor.

5. Carl and Chung wrote the _____ for the class play.

6. Everyone heard Beth _____ when she saw the alligator.

IF87103 *"Fun"damental Phonics*

Name _____

Splashing Fish

Read the poem. Draw a line under the words that begin with the blend **spl**.

Splash!

Splish!

I hear fish!

Write a rhyming title for the poem.

_____

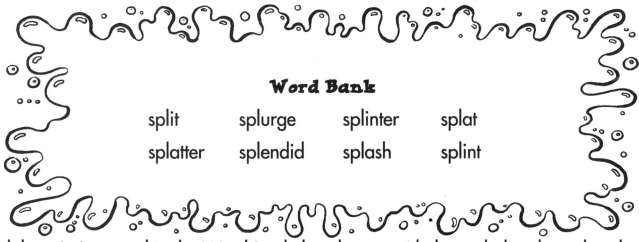

Word Bank

| split | splurge | splinter | splat |
| splatter | splendid | splash | splint |

Find the missing word in the Word Bank that rhymes with the underlined word and makes sense in the sentence. Write the word on the line.

1. Carry the <u>platter</u> carefully so you will not _____ the gravy.

2. Morgan made a <u>bid</u> on the _____ picture.

3. When Maria's finger hurt, it was the first <u>hint</u> that she needed a _____ .

4. We can each have a little <u>bit</u> if we _____ the cookie.

5. This <u>winter</u>, I fell against a tree and got a _____ .

6. After a quick <u>dash</u>, Lee jumped into the pool with a _____ !

7. May suddenly had the <u>urge</u> to _____ on a new pair of shoes.

8. "_____ !" went the cupcakes on the <u>mat</u>.

IF87103 "Fun"damental Phonics

Name _____

Spring Has Sprung

Write the blend **spr** on the lines to complete the words in the poem and the Word Bank. Read the poem.

_____ ing has _____ung!
_____ing has _____ead!
A _____ay is _____inkling
My flower bed!

Word Bank

_____ee   _____ain   _____y
_____ingy   _____ang   _____out
_____inkler _____int   _____awl

Use the poem as a Word Bank. Find the correct **spr** word in the poem to answer each riddle.

1. I come after winter.   _____

2. I am a fine jet of water.   _____

3. I am how you keep grass green. _____

4. I am what you do with butter. _____

Find each missing word in the Word Bank to complete each sentence and write it in the puzzle.

Across:

3. Dad went on a shopping _____ at the hardware.

4. That rubber ball is so _____ that it bounces everywhere.

5. Soon the plants will _____ leaves.

6. The kitten _____ out of the box and ran off.

7. Juan and Peter _____ on the floor when they draw.

8. Be careful not to _____ your ankle.

Down:

1. Meg will _____ around the track twice.

2. That old dog is quite _____ .

4. Please move the _____ to water the roses.

IF87103 "Fun"damental Phonics

Name _____

Squirrel Square

Write the blend **squ** on the lines to complete the words in the poem. Read the poem.

In _____ irrel _____ are,
The _____irrels there
_____eak and _____awk,
_____eal and talk!

Use the poem as a Word Bank. Find the correct **squ** words to complete each sentence and then write them in the puzzle.

Across:

2. The mouse gave a ____ and ran into the hole.
3. A shape with four equal sides is a ____ .
4. That gray ____ ate all our bird seed!

Down:

1. The plump piglet let out a ____ when he couldn't find his mother.
3. That ____ was made by a hawk.

Word Bank

squint	squirt	squishy
squeeze	squash	squad

Find the missing **squ** word in the Word Bank to complete each sentence.

1. Carla and Maria both tried out for the cheerleading _____ .

2. Mark helped _____ oranges for fresh juice.

3. We had to _____ as we walked into the sunlight.

4. Many people like baked _____ on Thanksgiving.

5. I want to _____ some mustard on my hot dog.

6. Bob doesn't like to hold worms because they feel _____ .

IF87103 "Fun"damental Phonics

Name _____

Stretch Some String

Write the blend **str** on the lines to complete the words in the poem. Read the poem.

I can _____etch _____ing,
_____etch it _____aight and long.
Can you _____etch _____ing?
You must be very _____ong!

Use the poem for a Word Bank. Find the **str** word to complete each sentence.

1. Paul needs some _____ to tie up the box.

2. Jane is so _____ that she carries six books at a time!

3. How far can you _____ your arms?

4. We had to stand in a _____ line.

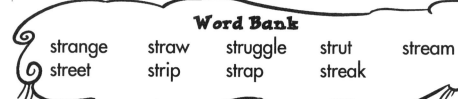

Word Bank

strange	straw	struggle	strut	stream
street	strip	strap	streak	

Find the missing **str** word in the Word Bank to complete each rhyme. Write the word on the line.

1. The peacock came out of the <u>hut</u>. Look at his proud, prancing _____ !

2. Always smile at those you <u>meet</u> when you pass them on the _____ .

3. As the kittens tried to <u>snuggle</u>, it looked like quite a _____ .

4. They used a wooden <u>beam</u> as a bridge across the _____ .

5. The storm clouds over the <u>range</u> made a green glow that was _____ .

6. Watch out! Don't <u>trip</u> on that metal _____ .

7. The hen used its <u>claw</u> to find food in the _____ .

8. Look at that parrot's <u>beak</u>; you will see a bright orange _____ .

9. The baby's <u>cap</u> needs a _____ .

Name _____

Thread the Blends

Write the blend **thr** on the lines to complete the words in the poem. Read the poem.

I _____ew _____ee _____eads
_____ough the air.
I _____ew _____ee _____eads,
But where?

Use the poem as a Word Bank. Find the **thr** word to complete each sentence and write it in the puzzle.

Across:

1. Maria ____ the ball to first base just in time.
2. We must walk ____ the park to reach the pond.
3. Mom cut the loose ____ off her skirt.

Down:

1. Chung, Mark, and I took the first ____ seats.

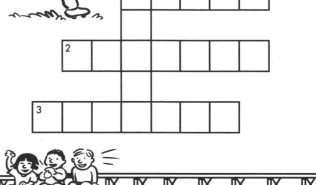

Write **thr** to complete these words.

_____ ill   _____ow   _____ob   _____oat   _____ifty

Write the missing **thr** word from above to complete each sentence.

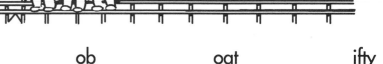

1. Please _____ this in the trash.
2. Brett couldn't go sledding because he had a sore _____ .
3. Alesha was so _____ , she saved forty dollars.
4. Sara's thumb began to _____ after she slammed the door on it.
5. The new roller coaster gave us all a big _____ !

IF87103 *"Fun"damental Phonics*

Name _____

Choose Your Cake

Write the blend **ch** on the lines to complete the words in the poem. Read the poem.

I _____oose the cake

I _____ew with ease:

_____ocolate _____ip

_____erry _____eese!

My _____eerful _____oice

Is one _____unk, please,

Of _____ocolate _____ip

_____erry _____eese!

Use the poem as a Word Bank. Find the **ch** word to complete each sentence and write it in the puzzle.

Across:

5. The cake was iced with rich, dark _____ .

6. Please put a sweet, red _____ on top of the sundae.

7. Sam wants a big _____ of cake.

Down:

1. Which kind of cheesecake would you _____ ?

2. My _____ would be a piece of cherry cheesecake.

3. We sprinkle _____ on top of pizza.

4. Everyone at the party was very _____ .

5. Cheesecake is easy to _____ .

6. Here's a chocolate _____ left over from the cookies.

IF87103 *"Fun"damental Phonics*

Name _____

Share a Wish

Write the digraph **sh** on the lines to complete the words in the poems. Read the poems.

I _____all not _____out,

I _____all not _____ove,

I'll _____ine my _____oes

And _____are my love!

Each and every fi_____ ,

Has the same wi_____

To swi_____ in the
   water and

Not be on a di_____ !

Use the poems as Word Banks. Choose the correct **sh** word to answer the riddles.

1. This is a call. _____
2. This is a hope. _____
3. To move with a hissing sound. _____
4. This is a plate or bowl. _____
5. To do this is most thoughtful. _____
6. This is the sun's job. _____
7. This means "to push past." _____
8. These go on your feet. _____
9. This swims in seas and lakes. _____

What will you wish for on your next birthday?

_____

_____

IF87103 *"Fun"damental Phonics*

Name _____

These Teeth

Write the digraph **th** on the lines to complete the words in the poems. Read the poems.

_____ese are ours,

_____ose are _____eirs.

Through _____is and

_____at,

The whole group shares!

The tee_____

In your mou_____

Grow nor_____

And sou_____!

_____at's the tru_____

For every too_____!

Use the poems as Word Banks. Find the missing **th** word that rhymes with the underlined word and makes sense. Write the word on the line.

1. The pioneers went <u>forth</u> on the trail heading _____ .

2. In a strong <u>breeze</u>, we can fly kites like _____

3. I <u>suppose</u> that I like _____ .

4. The dog shredded the <u>wreath</u> with his sharp _____ .

5. Max bumped against the <u>booth</u> and has another loose _____ .

6. They drove to the <u>mouth</u> of the river, then turned _____ .

7. Ruth moved here from <u>Duluth</u>. Believe it or not, that's the _____ .

8. These big brown <u>bears</u> say this lair is _____ .

9. Did you hear a snake <u>hiss</u>? How did we get into _____ ?

10. My cat won't wear a <u>hat</u>. What do you think of _____ ?

IF87103 "Fun"damental Phonics

Name _____

Whisper

Write the digraph **wh** on the lines to complete the words in the poem. Read the poem.

_____isper your questions,   "_____at?" "_____y?"
_____isper and share: "_____ere?"
"_____ich?" "_____en?"

Write sentences using each **wh** word in the poem.

1. _____
2. _____
3. _____
4. _____
5. _____
6. _____

Write **wh** to complete these words.

_____ittle   _____eelchair   _____ether
_____ile   _____imper   _____iskers

Read the sentences. Write the missing word on the line.

1. Do you know _____ we are going swimming or hiking?

2. Megan sat in a _____ as she waited for the doctor to check her leg.

3. The cat's _____ twitched as it watched the bird.

4. Uncle Van can _____ a piece of wood into a beautiful carving.

5. We heard the puppy _____ at night.

6. Maria played in a soccer game _____ her brother played in a baseball game.

27

Name _____

Phone an Elephant

Write the digraph **ph** on the lines to complete the words in the poems. Read the poems.

Ele_____ant, ele_____ant

Is so alone.

I'll send him a _____oto

And call him by _____one!

Autogra_____!

Photogra_____!

Phonogra_____ , too.

I have every kind of gra_____.

How about you?

Use the poems as Word Banks. Find the correct word to answer each riddle.

1. This is what you use to call the lonely elephant. _____

2. This plays records. _____

3. This kind of chart compares things. _____

4. This animal is all alone in the poem. _____

5. This is what a famous person writes on his or her picture. _____

6. You need a camera to take one of these. _____

Write **ph** to complete these words.

_____easant   paragra_____   _____onics   telegra_____

Read the sentences. Write the missing word on the line.

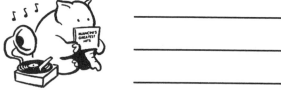

1. Write a _____ about thunderstorms.

2. Use _____ to help you sound out new words.

3. A _____ landed in the field near the lake.

4. Morse Code was invented to send messages over _____ wires.

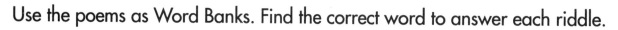
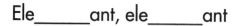

28

Name _____

Enough!

Write the digraph **gh** on the lines to complete the words in the poem. Read the poem.

Cou_____ enou_____

And it feels rou_____ !

Lau_____ enou_____

And life won't feel tou_____ !

Use the poem as a Word Bank. Find the **gh** word to complete each sentence.

1. We need to sand this board because it is too _____ .

2. The clown made us all _____ .

3. The steak was too _____ to cut.

4. Our class earned _____ money to go on a field trip.

5. The smoke from the campfire made us all _____ .

Write a rhyming poem about something that makes you laugh.

_____

_____

_____

_____

_____

_____

Draw a picture to go with your poem.

IF87103 *"Fun"damental Phonics*

Name _____

On the Knoll

Write **kn** on the lines to complete the words in the Word Bank.

Word Bank

_____ uckle   _____ee   _____ oll   _____ ife

_____ ew   _____ apsack   _____ eel   _____ ot

_____ock   _____ ow   _____ ight   _____ it

Use the Word Bank to complete the story.

Somehow, I _____ the hike would go badly. When I packed my _____ , I could not find my lucky jack_____ . I scraped a _____ on my hand. And when we crossed the rocky _____ and saw the dark clouds, I felt a _____ in my stomach.

It got colder and colder. Mrs. Lee, our leader, said, "I'm going to _____ down by this big rock and see if I can light a fire." I started to wish that Mom had_____ me a sweater last winter. We were all shivering.

"Get warm by this fire," said Mrs. Lee. "Then we will hike back to the bus. I _____ a shortcut." I was so cold, you could hear my _____s _____ together!

We got back to the bus just as it started to snow. Mrs. Lee was like a brave _____ from a storybook, leading us onward! From now on, I plan to read about nature in books . . . it's warmer!

30

Name _____

What Did I Write?

Write **wr** on the lines to complete the words in the poem. Read the poem.

What did I _____ ite?
I _____ ote a poem,
I _____ ote a song,
But I _____ ote no words.
Oops! I _____ ote it _____ong!

Word Bank

wriggle	wreck	wrench	write	wring	wrestle
wren	wrote	wrong	wrist	wreath	wrap

Find the missing **wr** word in the Word Bank that rhymes with the underlined word and makes sense in the sentence. Write the word on the line.

1. We will need a _____ to fix this <u>bench</u>.

2. After the kittens _____ , they like to <u>nestle</u> down for a nap.

3. Please hang the _____ <u>beneath</u> the rafters.

4. Everyone started to <u>giggle</u>, watching the kitten _____ under the blanket.

5. Will you please _____ this <u>cap</u> for Jenna's present?

6. Alesha will _____ a story about the <u>site</u> for the new park.

7. Carl hurt his <u>neck</u> when he was in a car _____ .

8. To make a <u>fist</u>, curl your fingers, not your _____ !

9. That _____ is one of <u>ten</u> in the tree.

10. Oops! He's playing the _____ <u>song</u>!

11. Please <u>bring</u> me the towel after you _____ out all the water.

12. Mom _____ a <u>note</u> to remind herself about the meeting.

IF87103 *"Fun"damental Phonics*

Name _____

Such a Sight!

Write **gh** on the lines to complete the words in the poem. Read the poem.

When the sun is bri_____t,
And the clouds are li_____t,
And the birds take fli_____t,
It's a beautiful si_____t!
But beware! At ni_____t,
It may cause fri_____t
When two cats fi_____t.
(Well, they mi_____t!)
Am I wrong or am I ri_____t?

Use the poem as a Word Bank. Use the **gh** words in the poem to complete the story.

One dark _____ , we sat around a campfire.
The campfire was warm and _____ . The
_____ from the flames cast shadows on our tents. We
thought it _____ be fun to tell scary stories. Ted told
an eerie story that gave everyone a _____ . Ted and
Mark started to _____ about the ending of the story.
Just then, an owl took _____ from a tree. It made us
all jump up! It was quite a _____ as the owl
swooped over our heads. After this last scare, we decided this was
the _____ time to go to bed!

Write a poem about night.

_____

_____

_____

_____

_____

IF87103 "Fun"damental Phonics

Name _____

Gnats and Gnus

Write **gn** on the lines to complete the words in the poem. Read the poem.

A _____at sat
Upon a _____u.
The _____at said,

"_____u, how are you?"

Write a tongue twister about a gnat and a gnu.

_____

_____

 **Word Bank**

| assign | gnarled | lasagna | sign | gnat |
| resign | campaign | design | gnaw | gnome |

Find the **gn** word in the Word Bank to answer each riddle.

1. This means "to quit." _____
2. This is noodles, cheese, and sauce. _____
3. This is a tiny bug. _____
4. This is a make-believe little man. _____
5. This is when something's twisted. _____
6. This is when something is given to you to do. _____
7. This shows you which way to go. _____
8. This is a pattern to make something. _____
9. This is a time when people hear speeches and debates. _____
10. This means "to chew hard." _____

IF87103 *"Fun"damental Phonics*

Name _____

Little Lamb

Write **mb** on the line to complete the words in the poem. Read the poem.

Poor little la_____ ,
You can't cli_____ a tree li_____
Or wiggle your thu_____
Or co_____ your wooly hair.
But, don't fret, little la_____ ,
You *can* give us wool—
So there!

Use the poem as a Word Bank. Find the **mb** word to answer each question.

1. Who will grow up to be a sheep? _____

2. What goes together with <u>brush</u>? _____

3. What is another word for <u>branch</u>? _____

4. What do you do to go up? _____

5. What goes along with four fingers? _____

Find the **mb** words in the Word Bank to complete each sentence and write it in the puzzle.

Across:

1. The squirrel will ____ to the top of the tree for an acorn.

3. Hold the pen between your fingers and your ____ .

4. The tiny ____ wobbled as it walked in the pasture.

5. Matt's hands were so cold that they were ____ .

Down:

1. Maria likes to ____ her little sister's hair.

2. The dog licked up every ____ that fell on the floor.

4. A robin built a nest on a ____ of the oak tree.

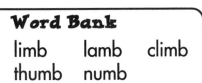

Word Bank			
comb	limb	lamb	climb
crumb	thumb	numb	

IF87103 *"Fun"damental Phonics*

Name _____

Pitch and Catch

Write **tch** on the lines to complete the words in the poem. Read the poem.

I'll pi_____ ,
You'll ca_____ .
Wa_____ the ball!
Nice stre_____ !
Good ca_____ !
Now, let's swi_____ !

Use the poem as a Word Bank. Find the correct **tch** words to complete each sentence and write it in the puzzle.

Across:

4. Everyone will ____ the movie.

5. Pedro had to ____ out his arm to tag Max.

Down:

1. Can you ____ a fly ball?

2. We ____ places after the third "out."

3. Bill likes to ____ fastballs.

Read the sentences. Find the missing word in the Word Bank and write it on the line.

Word Bank   fetch   scratch   ditch   batch   sketch   stitch

1. Rain flooded the _____ with water.

2. Let's bake a big _____ of chocolate oatmeal cookies.

3. Morgan uses a pencil to _____ pictures of birds.

4. No matter how much it itches, never _____ an insect bite.

5. Dad will _____ my new merit badge on my uniform.

6. My dog likes to _____ the ball from the lake.

35

IF87103 *"Fun"damental Phonics*

Nice and Cozy

Read the poems. Draw a line under the words containing the letter **c**. Listen to the sound the letter **c** makes in each word.

I'd like some rice,
And a pizza slice
With twice the spice,
And apple juice with ice.
So, what's the price?
That's nice!

The cute cuddly cat
Curled up on the mat,
All cozy and fat,
A comfortable cat!

Read each clue. Find the correct word in the poems and write it on the line.

1. This is how much spice I want on my pizza slice. _____

2. I want my juice to have this in it. _____

3. The cute cuddly cat did this on a mat. _____

4. I want some of this with my pizza slice and juice. _____

5. I thought this about the price. _____

6. I want this much pizza with twice the spice. _____

7. I want ice in this. _____

8. He is cute, cuddly, and curled on a mat. _____

9. I want twice as much of this on my pizza slice. _____

10. I asked about this so that I would know the
   cost of my food. _____

Write a sentence describing how to eat a slice of pizza.

_____

_____

Name _____

On Stage

Read the poem. Draw a line under the words containing the letter **g**. Listen to the sound the **g** makes.

When that bird was your age,
She left her golden cage,
Got to dance on the stage,
And made the front page!

Read the clues. Find the missing word in the poem and write it in the puzzle.

Across:

3. The bird in the cage was your _____ when she became famous.

5. The bird danced on a _____ .

Down:

1. The bird in the cage got to _____ on stage.

2. The bird that danced on stage lived in a _____ .

4. The bird danced so well her picture was on the front _____ .

Read the sentences. Find the missing word in the Word Bank and write it on the line.

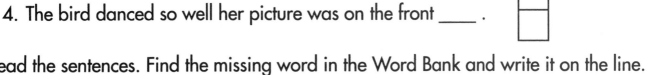

| Word Bank | engine | gym | garden | gentle |
| | giant | sugar | ginger | goose |

1. Beth planted cucumbers and beans in her _____ .

2. We are going to play basketball in the _____ after school.

3. We need _____ to sweeten the iced tea.

4. The _____ roared as the driver sped to the finish line.

5. A very tall person may seem like a _____ to a baby.

6. Please be _____ when you hold the little kitten.

7. A honking _____ waddled toward the pond.

8. Mom added some spicy _____ to the cookie batter.

IF87103 *"Fun"damental Phonics*

Name _____

On the Loose

Read the poem. Draw a line under the words containing the letter **s**. Listen to the sound the letter **s** makes.

The moose
And the goose
Are loose
In the caboose!

Find the words that complete each sentence and write it in the puzzle. Use the poem as a Word Bank.

Across:

2. This honking animal is loose in the caboose.
4. A moose and goose are loose in here.

Down:

1. This antlered animal is loose in the caboose.
3. This is how the moose and the goose are in the caboose.

Read the story. Find each missing word in the Word Bank and write it on the line.

Word Bank
salad
salty
seven
serve
soup
seat

We have _____ people in my family, so eating out is a big deal! We were_____ed around a big table by the window. When the waitress came to _____ our food, she got all mixed up! I got Mom's shrimp _____ , and Dad got a bowl of _____ instead of a steak. The baby got a plate of _____ pretzels, and she doesn't even have teeth!

Write a nonsense poem about a moose or a goose.

_____

_____

_____

_____ 38

variant consonant: soft /s/

Name _____

What Rose Chose

Read the poem. Listen for the sound the letter **s** makes.

Rose chose
To point the nose
Of the hose
On every rose.
She sprayed these and those,
And all the rest, I suppose!

Read the clues. Find the correct word in the poem and write it on the line.

1. This is the part of the hose that was pointed at every rose. _____

2. This is who chose to point the hose on every rose. _____

3. The roses Rose chose to spray. _____ and _____

4. Rose chose to point the nose of this at every rose. _____

5. Rose pointed the hose at every one of these. _____

6. Rose did this when she started watering each rose. _____

Read the sentences. Find the missing word in the Word Bank and write it on the line.

1. I knew this was the right puppy when he looked at me with his big brown _____ .

2. We need twenty-four _____ of soda pop for the picnic.

3. May we _____ have more potato chips?

4. Gretchen ordered a pizza with extra _____ on it.

5. Carl searched but could not find _____ homework.

Write a tongue twister about a rose.

_____

_____

_____

39

© Instructional Fair • TS Denison

IF87103 *"Fun"damental Phonics*

Name _____

Applause, Please

Write **au** on the lines to complete the words in the poem. Read the poem.

After _____gust,
There's a p_____se
Then it's _____tumn
Appl_____se, appl_____se!
Why?
Bec_____se!

Read the clues. Find the missing word in the poem and write
it in the puzzle.

Across:

2. The season after summer is _____ .

3. The performance received loud ____ .

5. She was late ____ she overslept.

Down:

1. ____ is a summer month.

4. There was a ____ before the next act.

Find the missing **au** word in the Word Bank that rhymes with the underlined word and
makes sense in the sentence. Write the word on the line.

Word Bank: (haunted   somersault   cause   vault   haul)

1. It's not my <u>fault</u> that we can't open the _____ .

2. Sam <u>taunted</u> me for being afraid to go into the _____ house.

3. <u>Paul</u> said he would be happy to _____ the wood for us.

4. When Dad said I could have a <u>malt</u>, I felt like doing a _____ !

5. Do you know the _____ of this long <u>pause</u>?

IF87103 "Fun"damental Phonics

Name _____

Mouse Law

Write **aw** on the lines to complete the words in the poem. Read the poem.

The mouse started to gn_____
On the hay and the str_____ ,
But then he made a face.
He said, "There is a mouse l_____:
Never eat r_____ str_____ .
Is there an oven in this place?"

Use the poem as a Word Bank. Find the correct **aw** word to answer each clue.

1. The mouse started to do this to the food. _____

2. The mouse asked for an oven because he never ate food that was ___. _____

3. The mouse was eating hay and this. _____

4. The mouse wouldn't eat raw food because of this. _____

Read the story. Find the missing **aw** word in the Word Bank to complete each sentence.

    The first day at the cabin, I woke up at _____
with a huge, sleepy _____ . There was dew on the
_____ that rolled down to the lake. I heard a
sharp cry, and saw a _____ in the sky. His
_____ were sharp, and his wings were spread
wide. As he flew away, a baby _____ came si-
lently out of the woods. She nibbled some clover. I stood very still so
I would not scare her. We both enjoyed the peaceful morning at the
cabin.

Word Bank

hawk
lawn
yawn
dawn
fawn
claws

IF87103 *"Fun"damental Phonics*

Name _____

After Breakfast

Write **ea** on the line to complete the words in the poem. Read the poem.

I spr_____d butter

On my br_____kfast br_____d,

Then rested my h_____d

And r_____dily r_____d.

Use the poem as a Word Bank. Find the correct **ea** word to complete each riddle.

1. This is filled with ideas.   _____

2. This is the first meal of the day.   _____

3. This can mean "a cover for a bed."   _____

4. This is what you did after you
   learned phonics.   _____

5. This means "quickly" or "right away."   _____

6. This is made from wheat flour.   _____

Read the sentences. Find the missing word in the Word Bank and write it in the puzzle.

Word Bank   heavy   instead   head   sweater   wealthy   thread

Across:

1. We went swimming ____ of rollerblading.
3. May knitted a beautiful ____ .
6. Max bumped his ____ on the cupboard
   door.

Down:

2. Dad needs blue ____ to sew on the badges.
4. The ____ king has a vault of gold.
5. The box of books was too ____ to lift.

IF87103 *"Fun"damental Phonics*

Name _____

Eight Reindeer

Write **ei** on the lines to complete the words in the poem. Read the poem.

_____ ght r_____ ndeer
Pulled a sl_____ gh
In my n_____ ghborhood today
_____ ght r_____ ndeer
Pulled their w_____ ght.
I grabbed the r_____ ns
To guide the fr_____ ght!

Use the poem as a Word Bank. Find the **ei** word in the poem to answer each clue.

1. This is where eight reindeer came today.   _____

2. This is what the eight reindeer pulled.   _____

3. Each of the eight reindeer pulled their own of this.   _____

4. This is the part of the sleigh I grabbed.   _____

5. Eight of these came to my neighborhood today.   _____

6. This is what I guided when I grabbed the sleigh reins. _____

7. This is the number of reindeer that pulled the sleigh. _____

Use the poem as a Word Bank. Find the missing **ei** word to complete each sentence of the story.

When we awoke, we found our whole _____ covered with fresh snow. _____ of us put on warm clothes and rushed outside to build a snowman. We all had to help push the snowballs because of their heavy _____ . Meish made a snow sculpture of a _____ with antlers. Carla used ropes to make a harness and _____ . The snow sculpture made everyone want to go for a _____ ride. Mr. Snowdon said that all of us at one time would be too much _____ for his horse to pull. So we took turns. It was a great snow day!

IF87103 *"Fun"damental Phonics*

Name _____

Have a Piece

Write **ie** on the lines to complete the words in the Word Bank.

sh_____ld

rel_____f

Word Bank

gr_____f

p_____ce

f_____ld

shr_____k

ach_____ve

br_____f

th_____f

bel_____ve

ch_____f

Use the Word Bank to help you find the missing **ie** word and write it on the line.

1. Alesha gave a sigh of _____ when she found her kitten.

2. Sara's _____ when her friend moved away made me sad, too.

3. Do you really _____ that some day we will fly to another planet?

4. Mrs. Ramirez said we could each have one _____ of candy.

5. Ahmed gave a _____, five-minute report about the book he read.

6. Long ago a knight used a _____ to protect himself.

7. The crowd gave a _____ when the loud firework exploded.

8. Mr. Edwards is the new _____ of the fire department.

9. Greg worked hard to _____ the award.

10. Chung and Carl watched the colts run in the open _____ .

11. Ms. Waters was upset when a _____ took her necklace.

Write a three-line rhyming poem about something you believe.

_____

_____

_____

_____ 44 _____

Name _____

Coast to Coast

Write **oa** on the lines to complete the words in the poem. Read the poem.

I don't like to b____st
But I travel in style.
I fly to the c____st
But we stop every mile

To have slices of r____st
Or some tea from the Nile,
Served with unbuttered t____st
Made by crocodiles!

Use the poem as a Word Bank. Find the correct **oa** word to answer each riddle.

1. This is "to cook slowly in the oven." _____
2. This is the border by the sea. _____
3. This is a bragging statement. _____
4. This is what we serve with tea! _____

Write **oa** on the lines to complete the Word Bank. Then read the poems and write the missing words from the Word Bank on the lines.

Word Bank

b____t   thr____t   g____t
c____t   fl____t

A silly _____
Jumped off a _____
To swim and _____ .
He had no _____ ,
So he got a sore _____ !

On the back of this paper, draw a picture to show what happened in one of the poems.

IF87103 "Fun"damental Phonics

Name _____

Loud Cloud

Write **ou** on the lines to complete the words in the poem and the Word Bank. Read the poem.

Oh, so l_____d!
Above my h_____se,
A rainy cl_____d
Was as gray as a m_____se
The thunder was so pr_____d
Of that lovely gray cl_____d
That it clapped right out l_____d!

Word Bank

m_____ntain

c_____ch   b_____nce

f_____nd   ab_____t

Use the poem and the Word Bank to find the **ou** words to complete the story.

We decided to drive to a ski lodge on our vacation. As we drove into the hills, we could see that the peak was covered with a low, gray _____ . The road leading up the _____ was very bumpy. Every time we ran over a pothole, the car would _____ . The tires rumbled _____ ly on the rocky road. The misty cloud made it hard to see. We almost turned back and went home!

We drove for two hours on that bad road. But then, we reached the ski lodge, a log _____ with a steep roof and a stone chimney. We were over-joyed to get there! We _____ our rooms, unpacked and then skied all afternoon. The owner of the lodge was very _____ of the fine, old place and told us all _____ its history at dinner. That night, we sat on the overstuffed _____ in front of the fireplace. We told ghost stories and popped popcorn. We were glad we had made it to the mountaintop!

IF87103 *"Fun"damental Phonics*

Name _____

Boil and Broil

Read the poem. Draw a line under the words that contain **oi**.

First let it boil,
Then add the oil.
Now wrap it in foil.
Next, let it broil.
Don't let it spoil,
Or drop it in the soil!

Use the poem as a Word Bank. Find the **oi** word to answer each clue.

1. This is what you add after boiling.   _____

2. Be sure you don't drop it in this!   _____

3. After you wrap it, the recipe says to do this.   _____

4. This is what you must use to wrap it.   _____

5. This recipe says that you must do this first.   _____

Write **oi** on the lines to complete the words. Use the Word Bank to find each **oi** word and write it in the puzzle.

Word Bank

c_____n   ch_____ce   j_____n   v_____ce

p_____nt   n_____se   m_____st

Across:

3. Add just enough water to make the batter ____ .

4. Dial the phone after you put in a _____ .

5. Ling will ____ us at the park.

6. Dad's ____ is so loud, it can be heard for blocks!

Down:

1. Do you hear a squeaky ____ ?

2. My pencil ____ broke.

4. Make a ____ between a hamburger or a hot dog.

IF87103 *"Fun"damental Phonics*

Name _____

Enjoy!

Write **oy** on the lines to complete the words in the poem and the Word Bank. Read the poem and the words.

Oh, b_____!
Oh, j_____!
A new t_____!

Word Bank

r_____al   ann_____

cowb_____   destr_____

l_____al   _____sters

v_____age   ah_____

Use the poem and the Word Bank. Find the **oy** word to complete each sentence in the story.

When my great-grandfather was a young _____ , he went on a sea _____ . He loved to talk about that trip. He met many famous people on the huge ship, including a _____ from a Wild West show and a _____ princess.

My great-grandfather's greatest _____ was to run very fast and then slide across the deck. He would shout, "_____ there!" to warn people to get out of the way. Although this would _____ the adults, nothing could _____ my great-grandfather's delight in doing this.

He had other memories, too. His father bought him a _____ ship at one of the shops on board. One night at dinner, he was served a big plate of _____ by mistake! When the trip was over, he would often play sea captain, with his _____ dog Banjo as his first mate.

Write a riddle about a toy you enjoy.

_____

_____

_____

_____

48

Name _____

Unknown

Write **ow** on the lines to complete the words in the Word Bank.

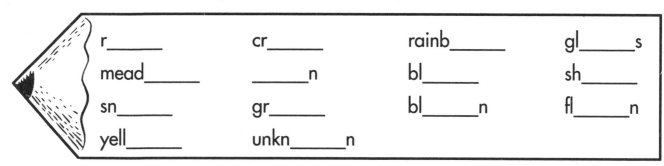

r_____   cr_____   rainb_____   gl_____s

mead_____   _____n   bl_____   sh_____

sn_____   gr_____   bl_____n   fl_____n

yell_____   unkn_____n

Read each poem. Write **ow** on the lines to finish each poem. Then in the box beside each poem, draw a picture to go along with the poem.

The sun gl_____

And melts the sn_____ .

Roosters cr_____ ,

Breezes bl_____ ,

Flowers gr_____

All in a r_____ !

The wind has bl_____n

The hat that I _____n ,

And now it's fl_____n

To a place unkn_____n!

In nature there is no sh_____

As beautiful as a rainb_____ .

Its curve glows with red and yell_____

As it reaches across the green mead_____ .

IF87103 "Fun"damental Phonics

Name _____

Take a Bow

Read the poem. Draw a line under each word that rhymes with **how**.

All you farmers, take a bow!
We'd like to thank you for our chow,
For how you rise to milk each cow,
Then feed the piglets with the sow,
And *then* go in the fields to plow.
Wow! We vow to thank you now!

Use the poem as a Word Bank. Find the **ow** word to answer each riddle.

1. This means "not later." _____

2. This is a mother pig. _____

3. This makes furrows in the soil. _____

4. This farm animal gives milk. _____

5. This is a promise. _____

6. This is bending from the waist. _____

7. This is another word for "food." _____

8. This means "in what way something is done." _____

Write a four-line rhyming poem about something that would make you say "Wow!"

_____

_____

_____

_____

IF87103 *"Fun"damental Phonics*

Name _____

A Few of the Crew

Write **ew** on the lines to complete the words in the poem. Read the poem.

The storm gr_____!
The wind bl_____ !
The ship fl_____ !
No one kn_____
What to do!
A f_____ of the cr_____
Cried out, "We're through!"
Then a giant canoe
Sailed into vi_____
And saved the cr_____ !
I think it's true.
Do you, too?

Use the poem as a Word Bank. Find the **ew** words to complete the story.

The _____ went aboard the ship the "Mermaid Song" at six o'clock in the morning to get ready for the voyage. A _____ eager passengers were already waiting at the gangway. The number of people in line _____ as it got closer to boarding time. Soon everyone was aboard the big ship. At four o'clock, the ship's signal _____ to warn that it was leaving port. All the passengers stood on deck to _____ the harbor. Several squawking seagulls _____ overhead as if to wish everyone "bon voyage." Everyone just _____ it was going to be a wonderful cruise!

Write a sentence about starting a voyage.

_____

_____

_____

IF87103 *"Fun"damental Phonics*

Name _____

My Special Jar

Write **ar** on the lines to complete the words in the poem. Read the poem.

> A toy c_____ ,
> A gold st_____ ,
> A sweet candy b_____ ,
> And a stange black stone
> As smooth as t_____ .
> They are all in this j_____ !
> How's that so f_____ ?

Use the poem as a Word Bank. Find the **ar** word in the poem to answer each riddle.

1. It means "the opposite of near." _____
2. A container to hold jam or jelly. _____
3. At night, this twinkles in the dark sky. _____
4. This is a kind of chocolate candy. _____
5. This black mixture is used on roads. _____
6. This is another word for automobile. _____

Write **ar** on the lines to complete the words in the Word Bank. Then read the poem and write the words where they belong.

Word Bank

c_____d
gu_____d
y_____d
h_____d

If it's not too _____ ,

Could you please _____

My baseball _____

While I play in the _____ ?

Write a list of five things you would keep in a jar.

_____

IF87103 "Fun"damental Phonics

Name _____

In a Lion's Lair

Write **air** on the lines to complete the words in the poem. Read the poem.

In a kingly l_____ ,

On a cozy ch_____

By a winding st_____

A p_____ of lions

Combed their h_____

Before strolling in the open _____

On a day sunny and f_____ .

Use the poem as a Word Bank. Find the word that answers each clue and write it in the puzzle.

Across:

2. Another word for a lion's den.

3. Something to sit on.

6. Light in color.

7. What we breathe.

Down:

1. Used to get from one floor to another.

4. This needs to be brushed and combed.

5. This means "a set of two."

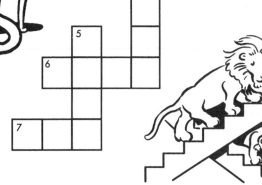

Write a poem about a pair of lions.

_____

_____

_____

_____

_____

IF87103 *"Fun"damental Phonics*

Name _____

Do You Dare?

Write **are** on the lines to complete the words in the poem. Read the poem.

Mrs. H_____ said to Mrs. M_____ ,
"I am going to Delaw_____ Squ_____."
Said Mrs. M_____ to Mrs. H_____ ,
"Well, I never! I decl_____ !
I'm also going to Delaw_____ Squ_____ !
C_____ to sh_____ the taxi f_____ ?"

Read the clues. Find the correct word in the poem and write it on the line.

1. She asked Mrs. Hare if she wanted to share taxi fare. _____

2. This is what Mrs. Mare wanted to share with Mrs. Hare. _____

3. Mrs. Mare and Mrs. Hare were both going to
   this square. _____

4. This is the word Mrs. Mare used to ask Mrs. Hare if
   she would like to share a taxi fare. _____

5. Mrs. Mare was so surprised that Mrs. Hare was also   "I_____ !"
   going to the square that she used this expression.

6. She met Mrs. Mare on the way to the square. _____

7. Mrs. Mare asked Mrs. Hare if she wanted to do
   this with the taxi fare. _____

8. Mrs. Mare and Mrs. Hare were going shopping here. _____

Write a nonsense poem about a hare and a mare.

_____

_____

_____

_____

54

Name _____

Observe

Write **er** on the lines to complete the words in the poem. Read the poem

Trees we cons_____ve,
Jams we pres_____ve,
Treats we des_____ve,
Seats we res_____ve,
Rules we obs_____ve,
And foods we s_____ve!

Read the clues. Find the correct word in the poem and write it on the line.

1. When we make strawberries into jam, we do this. _____
2. This means when we merit an award. _____
3. We do this to bring food to the table. _____
4. We do this when we don't waste resources. _____
5. We do this when we buy tickets for a concert. _____
6. Everyone needs to do this with rules. _____

Write a rhyming poem about a treat you deserve. Include a description of the treat and why you deserve it.

_____
_____
_____
_____
_____
_____
_____
_____

_____

55

Name _____

Hear, Hear!

Write **ear** on the lines to complete the words in the poem. Read the poem.

H_____ , h_____ for the _____ !
Your _____ is d_____ !
It lets you h_____
Both far and n_____

From y_____ to y_____ .
Never f_____
To praise each _____ !
Is that cl_____?

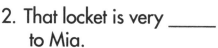

Use the poem as a Word Bank. Find the **ear** word to complete each sentence and write it in the puzzle.

Across:

3. A rabbit's _____ is longer than a cat's.

5. Did you _____ a creaking noise?

6. Sheila lives _____ the library.

Down:

1. The water is so _____ you can see the bottom.

2. That locket is very _____ to Mia.

4. In what _____ was the first space shuttle launched?

Read the sentences. Find the missing **ear** word in the Word Bank and write it on the line. Then circle the words in the puzzle.

1. The driver put the car in high _____ .

2. They will _____ the sheep next week.

3. Please don't _____ chalk all over the paper.

4. Cavemen could catch fish with a _____ .

5. It is a long wait if you are at the _____ of a line.

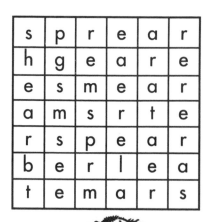

s	p	r	e	a	r
h	g	e	a	r	e
e	s	m	e	a	r
a	m	s	r	t	e
r	s	p	e	a	r
b	e	r	l	e	a
t	e	m	a	r	s

Word Bank

gear
smear
spear
shear
rear

IF87103 "Fun"damental Phonics

Name _____

Whirl Around

Write **ir** on the lines to complete the words in the poems. Read the poems. Then write a title on the line above each poem.

_____

Flower g_____l,
How your flowers tw_____l,
And wh_____l, and sw_____l!

_____

If you get d_____t
On a sh_____t or a sk_____t,
Just take water
And squ_____t, squ_____t, squ_____t!

Read the sentences. Find the missing word in the poems and write it on the line.

1. Patrick planted seeds after he dug holes in the _____ .

2. We watched the water _____ around as it went down the drain.

3. May spilled lemonade all over her pleated _____ .

4. On a hot day, it is fun to _____ each other with water.

5. That new _____ plays the piano very well.

6. A strong gust of wind made the leaves _____ up into the air.

7. Mark wore his new plaid _____ to the game.

8. Can you _____ a baton?

Read the words in the Word Bank. Write a sentence using each of the words.

Word Bank	circus	squirrel	firm	squirm

1. _____

2. _____

3. _____

4. _____

IF87103 *"Fun"damental Phonics*

Name _____

Picture This

Write **ure** on the lines to complete the words in the poem. Read the poem.

If you pict_____
Your fut_____
As an advent_____
Simple and p_____,
I fig_____
No matter what,
You're s_____
to end_____!

Use the poem as a Word Bank. Find the **ure** word in the poem to complete each sentence in the letter.

Dear Sara,

    Thank you for the letter and _____s you sent from your trip to Australia. I feel _____ that the memory of this trip will _____ after you are back home. The photo of the natural spring is beautiful. The water looks so clear and _____ . From your letter, I _____ that you have traveled two hundred miles a day! What an _____ it must be to drive through the outback and see kangaroos right by the road!

    I hope that someday in the _____ , you can come to Korea and visit me.

Your pen pal,
Hwa-Young

Write a sentence about an adventure you would like to have.

_____

_____

_____

58

Name _____

An Underwater Adventure

Read the compound word. On the lines, write the two words that make up each compound word. Then use the compound words to complete the story.

1. seafood _____

2. newspaper _____
   _____

3. notebook _____
   _____

4. smokestack _____
   _____

5. boathouse _____
   _____

6. seashell _____
   _____

7. seagull _____
   _____

8. toolbox _____
   _____

9. underwater _____
   _____

10. seaweed _____
    _____

11. sunburn _____
    _____

12. starfish _____
    _____

Use the compound words from the list to complete the story.

Taro and Tori read an article in the _____ about a ship that sank near their home. They called Uncle Ken. He told them to meet him at the _____ where he kept his salvage boat.

They ran down the dock where people were selling shrimp and other _____ . Uncle Ken was packing his supplies. He always took his _____ in case he needed to fix the engine. He also took food, water, and blankets. He checked all of his diving equipment and made notes in a _____ .

A white _____ flew overhead as they left the harbor. Smoke bellowed from the boat's _____ . Taro and Tori wore sunscreen so they wouldn't get _____ .

When they reached the spot, Uncle Ken put on his diving suit and dove _____ . Later, he told Taro and Tori, "I didn't find any treasure, but I saw many beautiful things. A _____ clung to a rock and looked just like a star in the night sky. A seahorse floated in some tall, green _____ . I found this beautiful striped _____ in the sand."

59

Name _____

Make the Connection

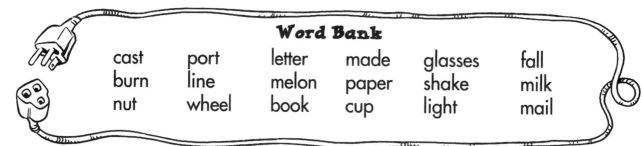

Word Bank

cast	port	letter	made	glasses	fall
burn	line	melon	paper	shake	milk
nut	wheel	book	cup	light	mail

Each word below is the **first** word of a compound word. Find words in the Word Bank that make compound words. Write the words on the lines. The first one is done for you.

news
newspaper
_____
_____

air
_____
_____
_____

hand
_____
_____
_____

butter
_____
_____
_____

sun
_____
_____
_____

water
_____
_____
_____

Choose one compound word from each group and use it to write a sentence.

1. _____
2. _____
3. _____
4. _____
5. _____
6. _____

Use the words from your lists to answer each riddle.

1. A place where airplanes land. _____
2. The clasping of two hands. _____
3. A tiny yellow flower. _____
4. Reporting on the hour. _____
5. A picnic-lunch dessert. _____
6. Skin that hurts from too much sun. _____

60

Name _____

Campground Compounds

Read each compound word. On the lines write the two words that were put together to make the compound word.

1. campground _____
   _____

2. outdoors _____
   _____

3. pinecone _____
   _____

4. backpack _____
   _____

5. overnight _____
   _____

6. firewood _____
   _____

7. footbridge _____
   _____

8. bullfrog _____
   _____

9. waterfall _____
   _____

10. grasshopper _____
    _____

11. bedtime _____
    _____

12. pancakes _____
    _____

13. campfire _____
    _____

14. footpath _____
    _____

Read the story. Write the missing compound words on the line.

Mark and his father love the fresh air of the _____ . They were excited as they planned an _____ camping trip. Mark put some food and trail mix in his _____ . Dad put juice, matches and a first-aid kit in his.

When they arrived at the _____ , they set up camp and gathered _____ for a fire. Then they went hiking on the _____ that led to the lake. They passed a rushing _____ . Mark saw a red squirrel grab a _____ and race up the pine tree. A _____ hopped ahead of them on the trail. Water flowed over rocks beneath them as they crossed a small_____ . When they came to the end of the trail, they watched the _____ .

Back at their camp, Mark and his father built a blazing _____ . It was so quiet that they could hear a _____ croak in the distance.

IF87103 "Fun"damental Phonics

Name _____

Baseball Fan

Read the story. Underline each compound word.

It was the afternoon of the big game. People hurried to find seats in the grandstand. My mother is the biggest baseball fan of all time, so of course we were there. "We have the hometown advantage," Mom said. She leaned forward to watch our team captain give a handshake to the Nutsville Flying Squirrels coach. Then she yelled, "Let's play ball!" I put on my sunglasses and sank down in my seat. I think Mom imagines she's a cheerleader.

The loudspeaker system was broken, so Mom was the loudest person in the stands. Even though she wrote every play in her notebook, she still had time to cheer. She nearly did a handstand when our team made a doubleplay to win! When she treated us to milkshakes after the game, we had to listen to her talk about the outfielders the whole time.

Choose ten of the compound words you underlined. Write down the two words that make up each compound on the lines.

1. _____

   _____

2. _____

   _____

3. _____

   _____

4. _____

   _____

5. _____

   _____

6. _____

   _____

7. _____

   _____

8. _____

   _____

9. _____

   _____

10. _____

   _____

IF87103 "Fun"damental Phonics

Link Up the Words

Name _____

Word Bank

sun	note	play	book	head	hide
out	camp	look	suit	cook	flash
under	bed	scrap	road	take	pillow

Each word below is the **second** word in a compound. Find words in the Word Bank that make compound words and write the words on the lines. The first one is done for you.

book
notebook
_____
_____

light
_____
_____

ground
_____
_____

side
_____
_____

case
_____
_____

out
_____
_____

Use the compound words above to answer these riddles.

1. You would want this if you were a bank robber. _____
2. You would want this when you were making your bed. _____
3. You would want to be here if you were a wild animal. _____
4. You would want to be here if you were on recess. _____
5. You would want this if your lights were out. _____
6. You would want this to write in at school. _____
7. You would want two of these on the front of your car. _____
8. You would go here to set up your tent. _____
9. You would want this to hold clothes for a trip. _____
10. You would go here if you were exploring caves. _____
11. You would need this if you had lots of books. _____

63

IF87103 *"Fun"damental Phonics*

Name _____

Till the Ground

Read the story. Draw a line under each compound word.

Farmer Jones gets up at sunrise. He has so many jobs to do! As he walks onto the porch of the farmhouse and looks around the barnyard, he can hear the chickens clucking. They are hungry!

After feeding all the animals, Farmer Jones climbs onto his tractor. He needs to plow the cornfield today. As he plows up and down the field, he thinks about how tall the cornstalks will grow and how good each ear of corn will taste. Then he plants the seeds. Knowing that the crows will want to nibble on the seeds, he stuffs an old shirt and a pair of jeans with straw. After he fastens the scarecrow to a post, he adds an old straw hat for its straw head.

The afternoon sunshine is hot, but Farmer Jones keeps working. Mrs. Jones is also busy. She has baked some homemade muffins with fresh, handpicked berries. Homegrown foods taste best to her.

At sunset, Farmer Jones and his wife sit on the porch, eating muffins and applesauce and drinking buttermilk. They smile as they watch tiny fireflies flit by the candlelight of their small lantern.

Write down ten of compound words that you underlined in the story. Then write the two words that make the compound word.

1. _____

_____

_____

2. _____

_____

_____

3. _____

_____

_____

4. _____

_____

_____

5. _____

_____

_____

6. _____

_____

_____

7. _____

_____

_____

8. _____

_____

_____

9. _____

_____

_____

10. _____

_____

_____

IF87103 *"Fun"damental Phonics*

contraction: /not/

Name _____

Put It Together

Write the contraction for each pair of words on the lines. Read the poems.

This soup does look good,

That soup _____ .
(does not)

This soup _____ !
(was not)

_____ this silly?
(is not)

_____ you, too?
(are not)

_____ you anything
(have not)

Better to do?

Use the poems as Word Banks. Find the contraction to complete each sentence.

1. Maggie has the flu, so she _____ going on the field trip.

2. We _____ been to the new amusement park yet.

3. Saturday _____ a good day for a picnic in the park because it rained.

4. May and David _____ excited about doing the yardwork.

5. That purple-and-green cake _____ look very tasty!

Write a four-line poem using the contraction to start each line.

Doesn't _____

Wasn't _____

Isn't _____

Aren't _____

_____ 65 _____

Name _____

Contract It!

On the lines write the contraction for the two words. Read the poems.

_____ ! _____ !
  (do not)   (do not)

Okay, I _____ .
        (will not)

_____ do this,
   (do not)

_____ do that,
   (cannot)

_____ ever touch!
  (must not)

With all the _____ s,
          (must not)

_____ s, and _____ s,
  (do not)   (cannot)

I _____ do very much!
   (cannot)

Use the poems as Word Banks. Find a contraction to complete each line of the poem.

My teacher says I _____ hurry
On my way to play.

But Mom tells me I _____ sleep in
Each and every day.

I _____ think that I ask for much,
But this I'd like to know:

If I _____ hurry out at recess,

Why _____ Mom let me go slow?

Write a sentence telling about something you **won't** do.

_____

Write a sentence telling about something you **can't** do.

_____

        IF87103 *"Fun"damental Phonics*

Name _____

Would You Like to Skate?

Contractions can be made using the words **have** and **would**.

Examples: I have becomes **I've**   **I would** becomes **I'd**

Read the contractions. Write the two words that were put together to form each contraction.

1. I've _____ _____   6. we've _____ _____

2. they've _____ _____   7. you've _____ _____

3. I'd _____ _____   8. he'd _____ _____

4. she'd _____ _____   9. they'd _____ _____

5. you'd _____ _____   10. we'd _____ _____

Read the sentences. Circle the two words that can be put together to make a contraction. Then write the contraction for the two words on the line.

1. I have always wanted to go skating.   _____

2. We have decided to go on Saturday.   _____

3. Megan and Seth said they would like to go with us.   _____

4. We knew we would have fun together.   _____

5. When Megan wobbled on her skates, Seth said,   _____
   "You have never skated before, have you?"

6. Seth said he would show Megan how to skate.   _____

7. Megan told him she would be glad if he could help her.   _____

8. I told Seth that I would like him to help me also.   _____

9. Seth said, "You would be a great skater with practice."   _____

10. The whole group said they would like to skate   _____
    together again.

IF87103 *"Fun"damental Phonics*

Name _____

You're Where?

Write the contraction for each two words on the lines. Read the poem.

_____ here.
(I am)

_____ aware.
(we are)

_____ here,
(you are)

But _____ not there!
(they are)

Use the poem as a Word Bank. Find the correct contraction to finish each sentence.

1. Alesha, Shelly, and Cam say _____ going ice skating.

2. I was late and now _____ going to miss the beginning of the movie!

3. Mark and I decided that _____ going to write the report together.

4. _____ going to like my grandmother's cottage.

On the lines write the two words that make each contraction.

we're _____ _____   they're _____ _____

I'm _____ _____   you're _____ _____

Use the contractions above to write a paragraph about a special place you would like to visit.

_____

_____

_____

_____

_____

68

Name _____

What Will You Be?

On the line write the contraction for the two words. Read the poem.

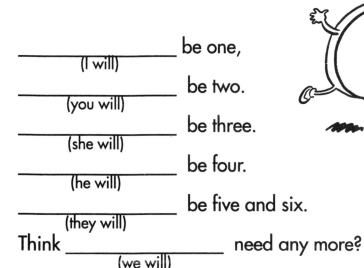

_____ be one,
(I will)

_____ be two.
(you will)

_____ be three.
(she will)

_____ be four.
(he will)

_____ be five and six.
(they will)

Think _____ need any more?
(we will)

Read the sentences. Find the missing contraction in the poem and write it on the line.

1. Dad told us that _____ need to leave early for the airport.

2. May walks by the library, so _____ return our books for us.

3. If you forget your lunch, _____ get very hungry.

4. I have to pick up the cake, so _____ be late for the party.

5. Sara and Cole have soccer practice, so _____ need a ride home.

6. Josh said _____ meet us at the baseball field.

Use the contractions in the poem to write a poem about a game you and your friends play.

_____

_____

_____

_____

_____

_____

69

contraction: /is/

Name _____

What's That?

Contractions can be made using the word **is**. **Example: that is** becomes **that's**

Read the contractions. Write the two words that were put together to form the contraction.

1. one's _____ _____   6. it's _____ _____

2. when's _____ _____   7. that's _____ _____

3. here's _____ _____   8. where's _____ _____

4. who's _____ _____   9. he's _____ _____

5. she's _____ _____   10. there's _____ _____

Read the sentences. Circle each pair of words that can make a contraction. Then write the contraction for the two words on the line.

1. When is the circus coming to town? _____

2. Here is a poster about the circus. _____

3. Look, it is going to be today! _____

4. Do you know who is going? _____

5. Michelle says she is going with Chung. _____

6. Clyde said he is going with his family. _____

7. Look! There is the circus coming down the street now! _____

8. Where is that elephant going? Oh, I see! _____

9. One is marching directly behind the other. _____

10. Wow! That is the greatest parade ever! _____

IF87103 "Fun"damental Phonics

Name _____

Unlike Others

The prefix **un** means **not**. On each line, write a new word by putting **un** in front of the root word.

1. saddle _____   8. stable _____

2. lace _____   9. load _____

3. clog _____   10. plug _____

4. wind _____   11. able _____

5. pack _____   12. lock _____

6. like _____   13. known _____

7. true _____   14. tie _____

Find the correct word from the list above to complete each sentence.

1. It is _____ just how many planets we have in our universe.

2. Can you _____ this knot?

3. Please _____ the horse before putting her in her stall.

4. Eva helped her mother _____ the groceries from the car.

5. We will use this liquid to _____ the kitchen drain.

6. It is _____ Joe to be so grumpy.   EXHIBIT A   EXHIBIT B

7. Mark hurt his leg and is _____ to run in the race Saturday.

8. Maybe this key will _____ the treasure chest.

9. After the trip, Dad asked us to _____ our own suitcases.

10. It is _____ that the world is flat.

11. Be sure to _____ the lamp before you fix the cord.

12. This rickety old ladder is too _____ to climb.

13. We will have to _____ this rope before we can use it.

14. Please help your little sister _____ her sneakers.

IF87103 "Fun"damental Phonics

Name _____

Repeat It!

The prefix **re** means **again**. On each line, write a new word by putting **re** in front of the root word.

1. lock _____
2. build _____
3. read _____
4. wrap _____
5. glue _____
6. stack _____
7. connect _____

8. fold _____
9. test _____
10. heat _____
11. appear _____
12. pack _____
13. sew _____
14. copy _____

Repeat Repeat Repeat Repeat Repeat Repeat Repeat Repeat Repeat Repeat Repeat

Find the correct word from the list above to complete each sentence.

1. Carol's paper was so messy that she had to _____ it.

2. The picture would not stay on the paper, so Pat had to _____ it.

3. David ripped his shirt, so Mom will have to _____ it.

4. After the tornado, we had to _____ the tool shed.

5. The magic act made a lion vanish and then _____ .

6. Chung helped her aunt _____ all the blankets.

7. The puppy knocked over the boxes, but Pete will _____ them.

8. Dad will _____ the cold soup.

9. Mrs. Ramirez said she would _____ the package.

10. It took two hours before they could _____ the power.

11. Sara had to _____ her suitcase to get everything in it.

12. "Please _____ the story," said Mrs. Patten.

Name _____

Impossible!

The prefixes **in, im,** and **ir** all meant **not**. Read the words. Draw a line under the prefix of each word.

impossible	informal	immobile
impatient	irregular	irresponsible
inactive	irresistible	invisible
improper	inaccurate	imperfect

Use the list as a Word Bank. Find the correct word to complete each sentence.

1. It is _____ even for a weightlifter to lift a ton.

2. The chipped handle made the pitcher _____ .

3. The computer is _____ because the software isn't loaded yet.

4. Megan was _____ when she left her coat on the playground.

5. Screaming in a library is _____ behavior.

6. The picnic will be _____ , so feel free to wear shorts or jeans.

7. The smell of fresh-baked cookies is _____ .

8. Sara was so _____ that she stormed out of the house without her brother.

9. The doctor was worried about her _____ heartbeat.

10. It is _____ to say that <u>everyone</u> likes chocolate ice cream.

11. Four flat tires will make a car _____ .

12. A thick fog made the boat _____ to those on shore.

IF87103 *"Fun"damental Phonics*

Name _____

Don't Disappear!

The prefix **dis** means **not** or **opposite of**. On each line, write a new word by putting **dis** in front of the root word.

1. appear _____
2. honest _____
3. trust _____
4. connect _____
5. obey _____
6. like _____

7. pleased _____
8. courage _____
9. respect _____
10. approve _____
11. believed _____
12. comfort _____

Find the correct word from the list above to complete each sentence.

1. Pete's broken ankle caused him some _____ .

2. It is _____ to take something that does not belong to you.

3. Sara must really _____ vegetables.

4. How did the magician make the rabbits _____ ?

5. You should not show _____ to those in authority.

6. The repairman had to _____ the cable from the television set.

7. I _____ that character in the mystery I'm reading; I think he's lying.

8. I _____ of your plan to go to the mall by yourself.

9. Dad was very _____ that our puppy shredded his shirt.

10. The librarian will _____ people from talking in the library.

11. Why did Dan _____ Mom and go fishing without permission?

12. My teacher _____ my story that the dog ate my homework.

IF87103 "Fun"damental Phonics

Name _____

Follow the Signs

When you add the suffix **s** to a noun, it changes it to mean more than one.

1. cabin _____
2. guest _____
3. table _____
4. balloon _____
5. map _____

6. firework _____
7. car _____
8. can _____
9. invitation _____
10. hamburger _____

Find the correct words from the list above to complete the letter.

Dear Becky,

Mia and I had so much fun this weekend! She invited some of her friends to stay in her family's guest _____ for two days. We mailed _____ to everyone last week. On Saturday, everyone loaded their _____ to start the trip to the lake. Mia and I had marked _____ to show the right roads to take.

At the end of the driveway, Mia and I had tied a big bunch of red _____ to a tree. Nobody had trouble finding the right place to turn! By noon, all of Mia's _____ were here.

Uncle Joe cooked _____ , and Mia and I handed out _____ of juice to everybody. We sat at big, round _____ under the pine trees. When it was dark, we walked down to the lake to watch the _____ display. We had a wonderful holiday.

Love,
Eva

Name _____

Flashes and Crashes

To make a word plural when it ends in the letter **s**, **ss**, **x**, **ch**, or **sh**, you must add the suffix **es**. Write the plural of each word. Read the words out loud.

1. patch _____
2. wish _____
3. crash _____
4. glass _____
5. coach _____

6. brush _____
7. box _____
8. flash _____
9. stitch _____
10. bench _____

Find the correct word, singular _or_ plural, from the list above to complete each sentence.

1. Both _____ talked to their teams before the game started.

2. Brad carried out two _____ filled with mitts and baseballs.

3. Then he used a _____ to sweep the dirt off the bases.

4. Steve's uniform had a tear, so his mom sewed a _____ over it.

5. Both teams talked about their _____ to win the game.

6. Coach Green did not think Sara's cut would need any _____ .

7. Suddenly there were _____ of lightning across the sky.

8. Then there were loud _____ of thunder.

9. All the players ran to the dugouts and sat on the _____ .

10. One of the snack bars sent free _____ of lemonade to the players.

Read the words. Write a sentence using each of the words.

matches   dresses   brushes   switches

1. _____
2. _____
3. _____
4. _____

IF87103 "Fun"damental Phonics

Name _____

Picked and Packed

The suffix **ed** changes a verb so it tells something that happened in the past. This suffix has three possible sounds: "d" as in *called*, "t" as in *helped*, and "ed" as in *added*.

Read the words. Draw a line under the suffix **ed**. Then write each word under the sound that the **ed** makes in that word.

Word Bank			
turned	opened	planted	watched
listed	cleaned	talked	needed
packed	boasted	spelled	laughed

ed	**d**	**t**
_____	_____	_____
_____	_____	_____
_____	_____	_____
_____	_____	_____

Use the list above as a Word Bank. Select the correct word that rhymes with the underlined word to finish the poem.

When fall came, the apples were _____
The week before hay was <u>racked</u>.

We worked every day 'till the wheat was <u>gleaned</u>,
The chimneys were swept and the barn was _____ .

After that, we made plans and _____
As over the fields we rode and <u>walked</u>.

And as the leaves to scarlet _____ ,
We saw to it that a bonfire <u>burned</u>.

By that fire we told tales and _____ ,
With cider mulling and chestnuts <u>roasted</u>.

IF87103 *"Fun"damental Phonics*

Spring Cleaning

Name _____

Read the words. On the line write the word and add the suffix **ing**.

1. clean _____
2. plant _____
3. carry _____
4. dust _____
5. add _____

6. look _____
7. vacuum _____
8. rain _____
9. wash _____
10. lift _____

Read the sentences. Find the missing word that will correctly complete each sentence and write it on the line.

1. It's spring and time for _____ vegetable and flower gardens.

2. As soon as everyone goes outside, it starts _____ .

3. Mom says it's a good time for _____ the house.

4. Sharon grabs a rag and starts _____ the furniture.

5. Greg begins _____ the carpets.

6. Mike starts _____ the windows.

7. Harriet is _____ in the closet for toys she no longer wants.

8. She is small and has trouble _____ the heavy box.

9. Sharon helps her by _____ the box downstairs.

10. Just when we thought we were finished, we saw Mom _____ more jobs to the list!

Read the words. Write a tongue-twister using each of the words

staying   showing   painting

1. _____

2. _____

3. _____

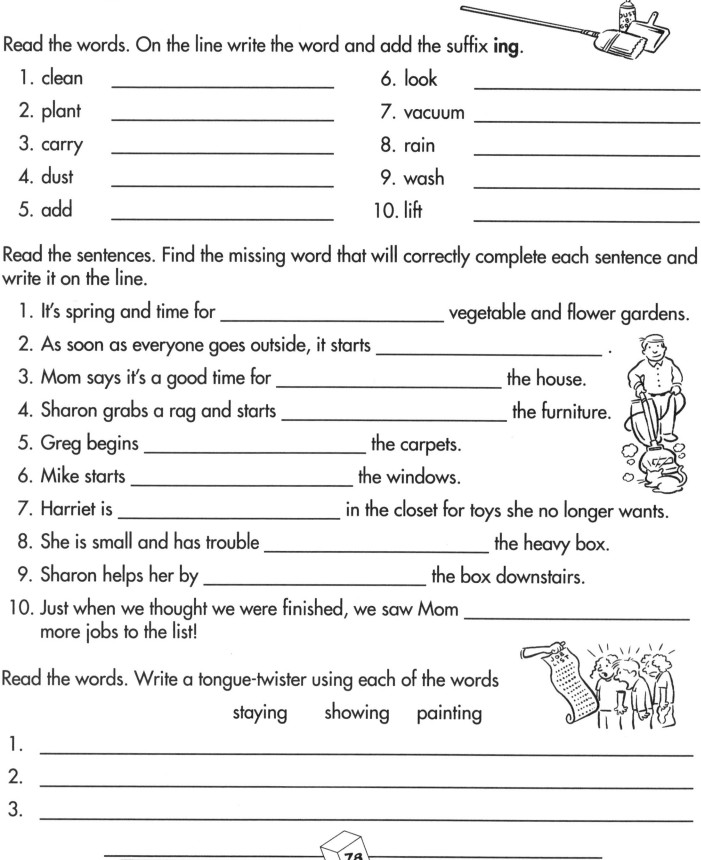

IF87103 *"Fun"damental Phonics*

Name _____

Read Silently, Please!

The suffix **ly** means **in a certain way** or **having the quality or characteristics of**. Read the words. On the line, write the word and add the suffix **ly**.

1. great	_____	6. friend	_____
2. foolish	_____	7. direct	_____
3. usual	_____	8. wise	_____
4. quick	_____	9. quiet	_____
5. brave	_____		

Read the story. Use the list above as a Word Bank. Find the correct words to complete the story.

Our librarian, Ms. Ray, is _____ and helps everyone. We know we must work _____ while in the library. Our class _____ goes to the library every Tuesday. On one visit, George acted _____ and ended up knocking a stack of books onto the floor. When Ms. Ray asked who was responsible, George _____ admitted it was his fault. He apologized and _____ picked up all of the books. He promised Ms. Ray he would act _____ in the future. Ms. Ray told George that she _____ appreciated his honesty. After the library time, George walked _____ back to our classroom.

Read the words. Write a sentence using each of the words.

tightly	strongly	gladly	timely	really

1. _____
2. _____
3. _____
4. _____
5. _____

IF87103 *"Fun"damental Phonics*

Name _____

Be a Word Inventor!

The suffixes **er** and **or** mean **a person who does something**. Underline the suffix in each word.

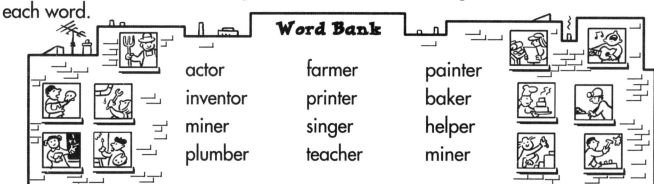

Word Bank

actor	farmer	painter
inventor	printer	baker
miner	singer	helper
plumber	teacher	miner

Read the riddles. Find the answer in the Word Bank and write it on the line.

1. This person is to a classroom as a captain is to a ship. _____

2. This person creates a different life on the stage. _____

3. This person pans for gold! _____

4. This person can change the color of your whole house. _____

5. This person's job is down the drain! _____

6. This person puts words and pictures on paper. _____

7. This person grows the food we eat. _____

8. This person needs to get up early to knead! _____

9. This person has a musical voice. _____

10. This person figures out new ways to get things done. _____

Choose three words from the Word Bank. Write a sentence using each of these words.

1. _____

2. _____

3. _____

IF87103 *"Fun"damental Phonics*

Name _____

Are You Able?

The suffix **able** means **can be done**. On each line, write the word and add the suffix **able**. Read the words out loud.

1. wash _____
2. enjoy _____
3. break _____
4. beat _____
5. like _____

6. move _____
7. reason _____
8. change _____
9. train _____
10. comfort _____

Use the list above as a Word Bank. Find the correct word to complete each sentence.

1. Old jeans are soft and _____ .
2. Sheets and towels are _____ .
3. Something fun is _____ .
4. Something made of glass could be _____ .
5. A friendly person is _____ .
6. Something you can lift and move is _____ .
7. A puppy can be taught, so he's _____ .
8. A team that can be beaten is _____ .
9. Something that changes often is _____ .
10. Something that makes sense is _____ .

Add **able** to these words: depend, like, and agree. Write a description of someone who has all three of these traits.

_____
_____
_____
_____

IF87103 *"Fun"damental Phonics*

Name _____

Get to the Root

A root word is a base word to which prefixes and/or suffixes can be added. A root word is a word all by itself. In the word **unwashed**, the root word is **wash**.

Read each word. Find the root word and write it on the line.

1. impossible _____

2. unimportant _____

3. dishonest _____

4. discovered _____

5. reaction _____

6. disagreeable _____

7. unkindly _____

8. reconstructed _____

9. misplace _____

10. planted _____

11. cleanable _____

12. cleaning _____

13. directly _____

14. disobeyed _____

15. unlocks _____

16. redoing _____

17. visitor _____

18. visiting _____

19. uncomfortable _____

20. builder _____

Here's a prefix–suffix machine! Put the root word in and add the prefix and suffix. Write the new word on the line.

Root Word	Prefix	Suffix	New Word
1. rail	+ dis	+ ed	= _____
2. pass	+ im	+ able	= _____
3. capture	+ re	+ s	= _____
4. break	+ un	+ able	= _____
5. fresh	+ re	+ ing	= _____
6. like	+ dis	+ s	= _____

IF87103 "Fun"damental Phonics

Name _____

Divide at the Root

Prefixes and suffixes are syllables by themselves. Syllables are chunks of words. Read the words. On the line write the words in syllables. Draw a straight line (—) to show where they are divided. The first one is done for you.

1. mislead   __mis–lead__

2. talking   _____

3. rewrite   _____

4. dislike   _____

5. comfortable _____

6. unmade   _____

7. teacher   _____

8. distrust   _____

9. ordering   _____

10. gladly   _____

Use the words above as a Word Bank. Find the correct word to answer each riddle.

1. Doing this in class is not always allowed. _____

2. This is another word for "happily." _____

3. This is the opposite of "like." _____

4. When you don't pull up the sheets and blankets on your bed, it's this. _____

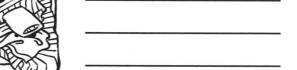

5. This is when you were led to the wrong place or idea. _____

6. This is when you have to do a story over again. _____

7. This word describes something soft and cozy. _____

8. This is the person who explains things in class. _____

9. This is when you tell a waiter what you would like to eat. _____

10. This is when you don't trust someone. _____

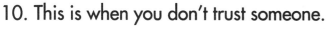

IF87103 "Fun"damental Phonics

Name _____

Pair of Pears

A **homophone** is a word that sounds just like another word, but it is spelled differently and has a different meaning. Read the poem out loud.

That pear and that pear,

That pair over there,

That pair of pears

Are they their pears?

No, they're ours!

Read the clues. Find the correct homophone in the poem and write it on the line.

1. This word is a contraction. _____

2. It is one of a pair. _____

3. Where our pair of pears are located. _____

4. This is what two pears are called. _____

Read the sentences. Find the missing word in the Word Bank and write it on the line.

| tea | plane | soar | shoo |
| tee | plain | sore | shoe |

1. Diana likes the _____ dress better than the frilly one.

2. Paula told the cat to _____ out of her garden.

3. Watch that hawk _____ toward the treetop.

4. Aunt May likes a cup of hot _____ on a cold day.

5. Mom places the golf ball on a _____ before she swings her club.

6. Jeff found his other _____ under the couch.

7. Our _____ landed smoothly on the runway.

8. The splinter made my finger _____ .

IF87103 *"Fun"damental Phonics*

That Makes Sense

Read the poem. Circle the homophones.

I was sent a whole cent
That I knew wasn't new,
The whole thing had a hole!
I thought, "What can I buy
With a cent with a hole?
No, I know! A doughnut hole!"

Read the clues. Find the missing homophone in the poem and write it in the puzzle.

Across:

1. The boy in the poem _____ his cent wasn't new.
5. This was in the center of his cent.
6. The opposite of "yes."
7. The opposite of "old."

Down:

1. The homophone of <u>no</u>.
2. This word means "all of something."
3. The homophone of <u>cent</u>.
4. This means "one penny."

Find the correct word in the Word Bank to complete each sentence.

| peek | peak | heard | herd | by | buy |

Word Bank

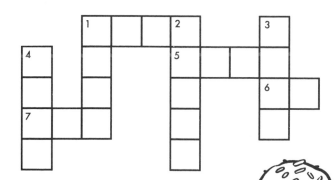

1. My little brother tried to _____ at his birthday presents before the party.
2. Jonathan helps his dad _____ the cattle to the new range.
3. They need to _____ tickets for the concert.
4. Mount McKinley is the highest mountain _____ in North America.
5. She walked _____ the bookstore on her way to school.
6. We _____ an owl hooting late at night.

IF87103 *"Fun"damental Phonics*

Name _____

Sail for Sale

Read the poem. Draw lines under the homophones.

Wood boat for sale!
It's ready to sail!
Its sail is for sale,
Too.
Two wood boats for sale!
Both ready to sail!
But where would
Two wood boats sail to?

Read the clues. Find the correct homophone in the poem and write it on the line.

1. The homophone for <u>would</u>.   _____

2. A piece of cloth that catches the wind.   _____

3. This number word is a homophone for <u>to</u>.   _____

4. This word means that something   _____
   is being put out to sell.

5. The homophone for <u>wood</u>.   _____

6. This word means "also."   _____

7. The opposite of "from."   _____

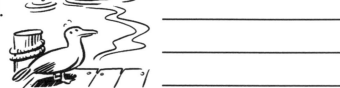

Write a sentence using each of these homophones.

      beat   beet   main   mane

1. _____

2. _____

3. _____

4. _____

IF87103 "Fun"damental Phonics

Name _____

Hoarse Horse

Read the poem. Draw lines under the homophones.

My horse was hoarse
And weak all week.
As we rode on the road,
He could hardly speak!
He sighed by my side.
As bored as a board.
But when I fed him hay,
Hey, his spirit soared!

Read the clues. Find the correct homophone in the poem and write it on the line.

1. He was hoarse and weak all week. _____

2. My hoarse horse and I rode on this. _____

3. My horse was hoarse and felt weak for this long. _____

4. My hoarse horse sighed as he stood here. _____

5. My horse had this medical problem. _____

6. My hoarse horse looked like this as he sighed
   by my side. _____

7. I fed this to my hoarse horse. _____

8. This is what I said when my hoarse horse's spirit soared. _____

9. My hoarse horse felt like this all week. _____

10. My hoarse horse and I did this on a road. _____

11. My hoarse horse looked as bored as this as he
    sighed by my side. _____

IF87103 *"Fun"damental Phonics*

Name _____

The Guest Guessed

Read the poem. Draw lines under the homophones.

The guest guessed
He should leave in a minute
As the maid made his bed
While he was still in it!

Read the clues. Find the correct homophone in the poem and write it on the line.

1. She made the guest's bed.   _____
2. He guessed he should leave.   _____
3. What the maid did to the guest's bed.   _____
4. What the guest did after the maid made   _____
   his bed while he was still in it.

In the letter, each two sentences contain a pair of homophones. Read two sentences at a time, find the homophones, and underline them.

Dear Zachary,

I could not wait to write to you about my trip. You would not believe the weight of my suitcase—I brought back so much stuff!

The last night we were in the city, we ate out at a restaurant in a castle. There was a knight in armor at the door!

The plane ride home took hours. Mom said we were lucky they served a good, plain lunch. It seemed so long before we were served our food. Then Mom tried to sew, and I read a whole book!

The pilot told us to peek out the window about an hour before we landed. We saw snow on the peak of a mountain!

See you soon—

Jason

88

Name _____

One Lead to Another

Read the poem. Circle the homophones.

> Two tall pencils had a race.
> The first led by its lead!
> But the second passed past,
> Erasing very fast.
> The second one won by a head!

Read the sentences. Find the correct homophone in the poem and write it on the line.

1. My brother's team _____ every game last season.
2. Our bus _____ by the new building site.
3. Chung read a book about Korea's _____ .
4. Which _____ of these shirts do you like?
5. Beth's pencil _____ broke in the middle of the test.
6. Gordon _____ the rest of the sprinters and won the race.

Read the poem. The homophones are mixed up! In the space with the numbers, write the correct homophone for each word.

In you're library   1. _____
Your not aloud   2. _____
                           3. _____
To talk allowed.   4. _____
And if books are late,
You'll fined   5. _____
You will be find!   6. _____

IF87103 "Fun"damental Phonics

Name _____

I Read in Bed

Read the poem. Draw lines under the homophones.

My eye turned red
As I read in bed,
For I read in bed
Until four.
But now I feel great
For I ate before eight,
And I'm not in a knot
Anymore!

Read the clues. Find the correct homophone in the poem and write it on the line.

1. My eye turned red because I did this in bed.   _____

2. I read in bed until this hour.   _____

3. This is what I did before eight.   _____

4. This turned red when I read in bed.   _____

5. This is what I'm not in anymore.   _____

6. This is a name to call myself.   _____

7. The color my eye turned when I read in bed.   _____

8. I feel great because I ate before this hour.   _____

Write a sentence using each of these homophones.

   heal   heel   reed   read   tied   tide

1. _____

2. _____

3. _____

4. _____

5. _____

6. _____

IF87103 "Fun"damental Phonics

Name_____

An Ant and His Aunt

Read the poem. Circle the homophones.

An ant and his aunt
Stare at the stair.
The ant sighs at the size.
The aunt says, "It's time!
It's our hour to climb.
Let's do it before the dew dries."

Use the homophones from the poem above to complete the poem below. Each pair of lines contains one pair of homophones.

When we go on a picnic, my Aunt May_____

At the _____ of our huge family!

She moans, "People will _____ as we walk down the _____s,

As we start off so happily."

Then, when _____ May finds a place to serve lunch,

She screams at the sight of black _____s.

She says, "The _____ has come to start all _____ fun,

So you must go back to the plants!"

Late in the day, our darling Aunt May hates to find the grass wet with _____

She says, "Let's do go home; please, let's _____!

The grass is too damp for our huge family camp,

But it was lovely to be here with you!"

IF87103 "Fun"damental Phonics

Name_____

The Hair of a Hare

Read the poem. Circle the homophones. On the lines below the poem, write the pairs of homophones.

Hear right here
The tale of a tail!
It belonged to a hare with long hair.
It was white as flour
And shaped like a flower!
His tail is a famous tale here.

1._____ _____   3._____ _____

2._____ _____   4._____ _____

Read the sentences. Find the missing homophone from above and write it on the line.

1. Beth needs two cups of _____ for the cookie batter.

2. She braided her long _____ every day.

3. Did you _____ that strange noise?

4. That monkey can swing by its _____ .

5. Pedro picked a bright red _____ for his mother.

6. Debbie is supposed to meet us _____ at seven o'clock.

7. The brown _____ hopped into the flower garden.

8. Did you read the _____ of the disappearing house?

Write a rhyming poem about a hare with long hair.

Use these homophones: hair   hare   they're   there   by   buy

_____

_____

_____

_____

IF87103 "Fun"damental Phonics

homophones

Name_____

Homing in on Homophones

Read the poem. Draw a line under the homophones.

Each flower in those rows
Is a rose, I suppose.
How do I know?
My nose knows!

Read the clues. Find the correct homophone in the poem and write it on the line.

1. The roses are planted in these.   _____

2. My face has two eyes, a mouth, and this.   _____

3. The homophone for nose.   _____

4. This is a type of flower.   _____

Read the clues. Find the missing word in the Word Bank and write it in the puzzle.

Word Bank bear blew roll seam wrap
bare blue role seem rap

Across:

1. Max will play the ____ of a knight in the play.
2. Sara will sew up that torn ____ .
3. We have to paint the sky ____ .
4. A big brown ____ walked out of the cave.
5. I need some paper to ____ Mom's present.

Down:

1. This ____ was baked today.
2. It doesn't ____ very hot outside.
3. The tree looks ____ without leaves.
4. The wind ____ dust everywhere.
5. Did the mail carrier ____ on the door?

6. Did the mail carrier ____ on the door?

© Instructional Fair • TS Denison

IF87103 "Fun"damental Phonics

On the Move

❧ Each student will need . . .

- one copy of "On the Move" gameboard and recording sheet (page 96)
- two sets of letter/sound cards (pages 105–106)

❧ Directions

- Say a word.
- Students place the letter cards on their gameboards to spell the word.
- Give a series of directions requiring the students to change one letter/sound at a time to form a new word.
- After each manipulation of the letter cards, have the students write the newly formed word on their recording sheets.

Example:

Say the word <u>can</u>.

Students place the letter cards on the gameboard.

Give the following directions.

| c | a | n |

- Take the /c/ off and add /m/.   man
- Take the /n/ off and add /p/.   map
- Take the /m/ off and add /t/.   tap
- Take the /a/ off and add /o/.   top
- Take the /t/ off and add /fl/.   flop
- Take the /o/ off and add /p/.   flip
- Take the /p/ off and add /t/.   flit
- Take the /i/ off and add /a/.   flat
- Take the /fl/ off and add /c/.   cat
- Take the /t/ off and add /n/.   can

When finished, students' recording sheets should reflect the list above.

© Instructional Fair • TS Denison   IF87103 "Fun"damental Phonics

✎ Extend the Activity

- Read a poem, either one of your own choosing or one from the worksheets in this book. Students identify the word families, one at a time, focused upon in the poem. Students manipulate the letter/sound cards to make the different word-family words used in the poem.

  Then have the students work independently to create other words that would belong to the same word family. Remind students to write the new words they have formed on their recording sheets. Extend this activity by having students experiment with changing ending sounds and then vowel sounds. Allow time for the students to share their word lists with the class.

- As students become more proficient at the manipulation of the sounds, select a starting word for them to use. Allow time for the students to manipulate the letters (beginning, vowel, and ending sounds) to create new words. Remind them to record every new word. When everyone has finished, have students take turns giving directions to the class on how they manipulated their letter cards to make the words. Classmates listen and manipulate their cards according to the directions given and then say the new word.

- Give each student two copies of the worksheet *On the Move* (page 97). Have each student select a starting word and write it in the race car. Then he/she writes the directions on both copies and the resulting word on only one copy. After everyone has completed the activity, have students exchange their directions papers. When the exercises are completed, each student returns the page to the original writer. That person then checks the page, using the "answer key" he/she wrote.

IF87103 *"Fun"damental Phonics*

On the Move

On the Move

Name _____

© Instructional Fair • TS Denison

IF87103 *"Fun"damental Phonics*

On the Move

Name of Person Writing the Directions: _____

Name of Person Completing the Worksheet: _____

Moves:

1. Drop the _____ and add _____ to move on to _____ .
2. Drop the _____ and add _____ to move on to _____ .
3. Drop the _____ and add _____ to move on to _____ .
4. Drop the _____ and add _____ to move on to _____ .
5. Drop the _____ and add _____ to move on to _____ .
6. Drop the _____ and add _____ to move on to _____ .
7. Drop the _____ and add _____ to move on to _____ .
8. Drop the _____ and add _____ to move on to _____ .
9. Drop the _____ and add _____ to move on to _____ .
10. Drop the _____ and add _____ to move on to _____ .
11. Drop the _____ and add _____ to move on to _____ .
12. Drop the _____ and add _____ to move on to _____ .
13. Drop the _____ and add _____ to move on to _____ .
14. Drop the _____ and add _____ to move on to _____ .
15. Drop the _____ and add _____ to move on to _____ .
16. Drop the _____ and add _____ to move on to _____ .
17. Drop the _____ and add _____ to move on to _____ .
18. Drop the _____ and add _____ to move on to _____ .

Ending Word: _____

IF87103 "Fun"damental Phonics

Shape Up!

❤ Each student will need . . .

- one copy of the "Shape Up!" gameboard and recording sheet (page 104)
- letter/sound cards (pages 105–106)
- 10 to 15 blank 3" x 5" index cards for compound words only

❤ Teacher will need . . .

- list of compound words (page 101)
- list of contractions (page 102)
- list of root words (page 103)

❤ Directions:

For compound words

- Students cut 3" x 5" index cards in half lengthwise.

- Write the beginning words of the compound words on the chalk board. Across from this list, write the ending words of the compound words. Be sure the ending words are in a different order so that the words across from each other do not match.

- Students copy one word on each 1½" x 5" index card strip.

- Students place the beginning word card on the gameboard. Then they match the ending word card to form a compound word.

- Students write the compound word on a line at the bottom of the sheet.
- Students then go to the next word on the list, and continue in this fashion until they have completed the entire list.

- When everyone has finished, have the students read the lists they have written.

IF87103 *"Fun"damental Phonics*

Extend the Idea

- Write five beginning words of compound words on the chalkboard.

- Students copy each word on a 1½" x 5" index card strip.

- Students place one word card on the gameboard and then use the letter/sound cards to spell out an ending word that will combine with the first word to make a compound word.

Examples:

air	p	o	r	t			airport
air	p	l	a	n	e		airplane
air	m	a	i	l			airmail
air	l	i	n	e			airline

Students write the compound words they have formed on the recording sheet.

Challenge

- Follow the same procedure as above except provide students with the ending word of a compound word.

- Students must then use the letter/sound cards to spell out the beginning words.

Example:

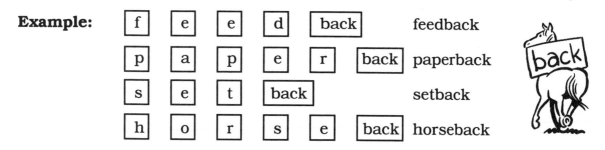

f	e	e	d	back		feedback
p	a	p	e	r	back	paperback
s	e	t	back			setback
h	o	r	s	e	back	horseback

For Contractions

- Write the two words that are combined to form a contraction on the chalkboard.

    Example: I will

- Students use their letter/sound cards to spell out the two words on the gameboard.

    Example: | I | w | i | l | l |

- Then they manipulate (remove omitted letters and add the apostrophe) their cards to form the contraction of the two words.

  Example: | I | ' | l | l |

- Students write the contraction they formed on the recording sheet.

For Adding Prefixes and Suffixes

- Write a root word on the chalkboard.

- Students use their letter/sound cards to spell the root word on the gameboard.

- Then they add a prefix and/or suffix card(s) to create new words.

- Students write the words they have formed on the recording sheet.

- When everyone has finished, have students read the words they have created.

  Example:

  Prefixes: (root word)   made | re | m | a | d | e |
                                   | un | m | a | d | e |

  Suffixes: (root word)   trail | t | r | a | i | l | ing |
                                    | t | r | a | i | l | ed |
                                    | t | r | a | i | l | s |
                                    | t | r | a | i | l | er |

IF87103 *"Fun"damental Phonics*

Word Lists for Shape Up!

Compound Words

Beginning Words	Ending Words	
snow	port	board
play	man	berry
back	thing	way
bath	one	
bed	storm	
door	ball	
day	house	
fire	book	
foot	room	
sea	time	
rain	boat	
sun	day	
air	light	
any	field	
every	door	
day	where	
hair	body	
over	ever	
night	line	
hand	box	
home	side	

© Instructional Fair • TS Denison IF87103 "Fun"damental Phonics

Word Lists for Shape Up!

Contractions

are not	that is
cannot	there is
do not	what is
did not	when is
does not	where is
had not	who is
have not	he will
is not	she will
must not	it will
should not	I will
could not	they will
was not	we will
were not	you will
will not	she would
would not	I would
they are	they would
we are	we would
you are	you would
I have	
they have	
we have	
you have	
he is	
here is	
it is	
one is	
she is	

IF87103 "Fun"damental Phonics

Word Lists for Shape Up!

please	open	tell	plant
certain	thank	usual	appoint
order	fear	dress	sharp
trust	bake	turn	attract
fair	write	fit	extend
happy	taste	sing	walk
fold	rest	wrap	direct
agree	skill	clear	teach
load	trace	harm	new
even	friend	salt	state
cover	glad	claim	paint
true	bright	sweet	loud
color	do	home	move
chain	swift	enjoy	comfort
fair	proud	own	invent
appear	part	care	correct
able	play	slow	kind
lock	watch	wear	act
made	cheer	quick	govern
like	wash	cure	elect
form	color	honest	long
read	sick	place	danger
frost	dance	melt	arrange
change	tie	pave	short
press	soft	safe	wind
built	print	pay	rail
fill	firm	sew	port

 IF87103 "Fun"damental Phonics

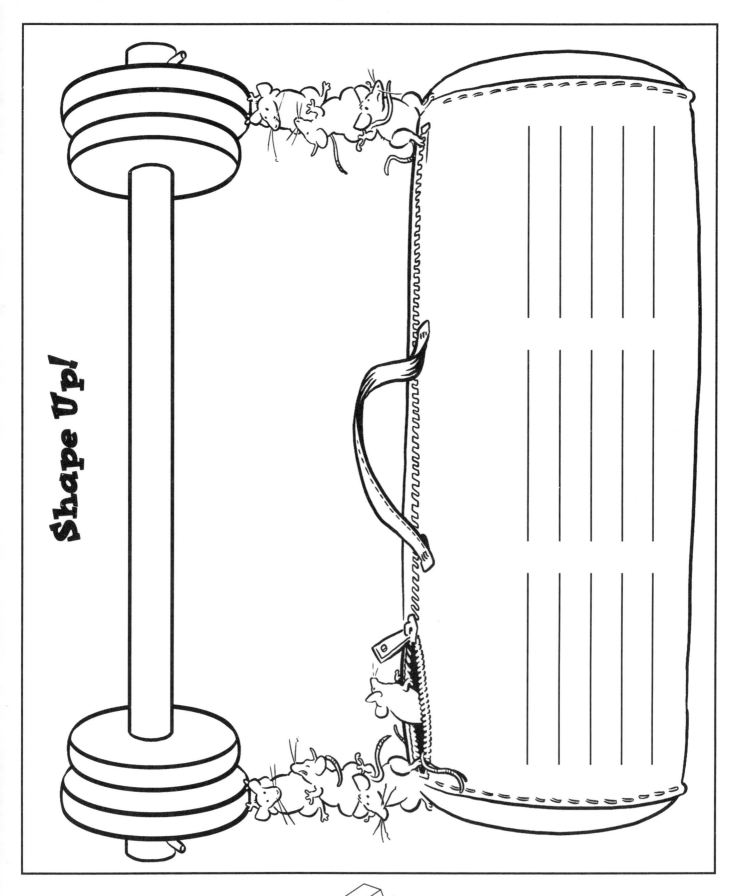

Shape Up!

IF87103 "Fun"damental Phonics

b	c	d	f	g	h
j	k	l	m	n	p
q	r	s	t	v	w
x	y	z	a	e	i
o	u	ch	sh	th	wh
ph	kn	wr	gh	gn	mb
tch	au	aw	ea	ei	ie
oa	ou	oi	oy	ow	ew

IF87103 *"Fun"damental Phonics*

Letter/Sound Cards: Make two copies for each student. Student cuts apart along the solid lines.

air	are	ear	ure	I	not
have	would	are	am	will	is
'	un	re	in	im	ir
dis	s	es	ed	ing	ly
re	or				

Additional Prefix and Suffix Cards

					en
non	over	mis	pre	ed	semi
mid	ion	able	ful	less	est

IF87103 *"Fun"damental Phonics*

Answer Key

"Fun"damental Phonics

Grade 3

Page 6

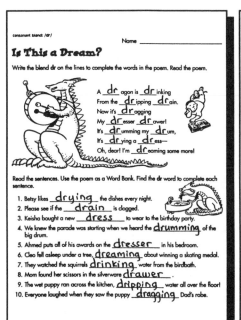

Page 7

Page 8

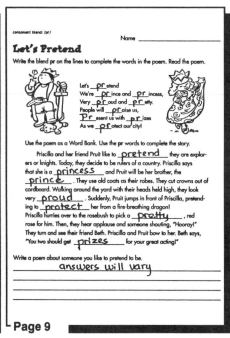

Page 9

IF87103 "Fun"damental Phonics

consonant blend: /tr/

Traveling Along

Name _____

Write the blend tr on the lines to complete the words in the poem. Read the poem.

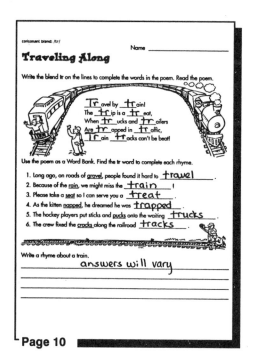

Tr avel by **tr** ain!
The **tr** ip is a **tr** eat,
When **tr** ucks and **tr** ailers
Are **tr** apped in **tr** affic,
tr ain **tr** acks can't be beat!

Use the poem as a Word Bank. Find the tr word to complete each rhyme.

1. Long ago, on roads of gravel, people found it hard to _travel_
2. Because of the rain, we might miss the _train_ !
3. Please take a seat so I can serve you a _treat_
4. As the kitten napped, he dreamed he was _trapped_
5. The hockey players put sticks and pucks onto the waiting _trucks_
6. The crew fixed the cracks along the railroad _tracks_

Write a rhyme about a train.
answers will vary
_____
_____

Page 10

---

consonant blends: /bl/, /sl/

Slippery Blasts

Name _____

Read the poems. Draw a line under the words that begin with the blend bl or sl.

Blizzard blowing
On our block!
Blow! Blow!
Blankets of snow,
Blasts of snow!

Never sleep on a sled!
Never sleep on a sled!
You'll slip and slide,
It's a slippery ride!
No, never sleep on a sled!

Read the clues. Use the poem to find the missing bl and sl words and write them in the puzzle.

Across:
3. Listen to the wind _____!
5. We have new _____ on our beds.
6. Let's go to the playground and play on the _____.
7. Don't _____ on the wet floor!
8. The icy roads are _____.

Down:
1. We live one _____ from school.
2. School was let out early because of the big _____.
3. I felt _____ of cold air whenever someone opened the door.
6. It is fun to _____ out in a tent.
7. Max likes to _____ down the snowy hills.

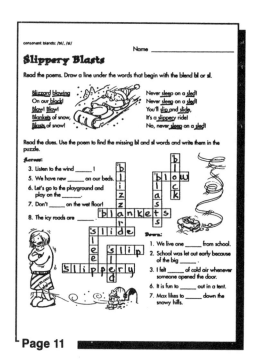

Page 11

---

consonant blends: /cl/, /gl/

Cleaning Up

Name _____

Write the blend cl on the lines to complete the words in the poem. Read the poem.

Cl imb up
And **cl** ean these **cl** ouds!
We can't see up here.
Take a **cl** oth
And **cl** ean up **cl** ose
Until each **cl** oud is **cl** ear!

Draw a line under words that begin with the blend gl. Read the poem.

Gloves can glide
Over glass,
It's true,
Unless the glass
Has globs
Of glue!

Use the poems as Word Banks. Find the correct cl or gl word to solve each riddle.

1. These float in the sky. _clouds_
2. These fit on your hands. _gloves_
3. This sticks things together. _glue_
4. This is used to make clothing. _cloth_
5. This is clear and can break. _glass_
6. This is what you do on ice skates. _glide_
7. This is the opposite of "far away." _close_

Page 12

---

consonant blends: /fl/, /pl/

Flies and Plums

Name _____

Read the poems. Draw a line under the words that begin with the blend fl or pl.

The fly flew to the flower,
The fly flew to the floor.
The fly flipped,
The fly flopped,
The fly flew out the door!

Please place those plump plums
On my paper plate.
I plan to eat plenty!
Place one, place two,
Plus three, plus four,
Until my plate holds twenty!

Use the poems as Word Banks. Find the missing fl or pl words that will rhyme with the underlined word and make sense. Write the words on the lines.

1. I'm sure twenty cakes will be _plenty_ for the bake sale.
2. Martha wished she knew where the geese _flew_
3. When we opened the door, we found crumbs on the _floor_
4. Mom found just the right _place_ to store the old lace.
5. Please don't fuss—we invited Russ _plus_ Gus!
6. Nate filled his _plate_ with chicken and salad.
7. Oh, _please_! Use a tissue when you sneeze!
8. No matter how hard you try, you are not a bird; you cannot _fly_
9. Mom always hums when she is picking ripe _plums_
10. A bright yellow _flower_ grew by the tower.
11. Their holiday _plan_ was to get a tan.

Page 13

© Instructional Fair • TS Denison

108

IF87103 "Fun"damental Phonics

consonant blends: /sk/, /st/

Name _____

Keep in Step

Read the poems. Draw a line under the words that begin with the blend sk or st.

To ski well
Takes special skills,
To skip and skate
And skid down hills.

Stop! Don't step!
Stay! Stand still!
Stop! Don't stir!
Stay! Steer clear!

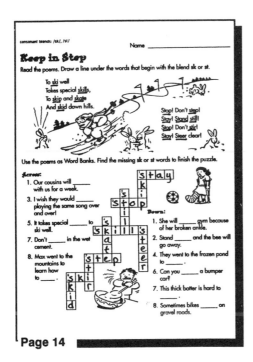

Use the poems as Word Banks. Find the missing sk or st words to finish the puzzle.

Across:
1. Our cousins will ____ with us for a week.
3. I wish they would ____ playing the same song over and over!
5. It takes special ____ to ski well.
7. Don't ____ in the wet cement.
8. Max went to the mountains to learn how to ____.

Down:
1. She will ____ gym because of her broken ankle.
2. Stand ____ and the bee will go away.
4. They went to the frozen pond to ____.
6. Can you ____ a bumper car?
7. This thick batter is hard to ____.
8. Sometimes bikes ____ on gravel roads.

Puzzle answers: stay, ski, stop, still, skis, skills, steer, skate, step, stir, skid

---

consonant blends: /sm/, /sp/

Name _____

Spinning Along

Read the poems. Draw a line under the words that begin with the blend sm or sp.

Smell the soup.
Smack your lips.
Small smile,
Big smile,
Smooth soup in smug sips!

Without a single spatter,
I can spin spaghetti on my spoon.
Oops! A big spaghetti spill!
I guess I spoke too soon!

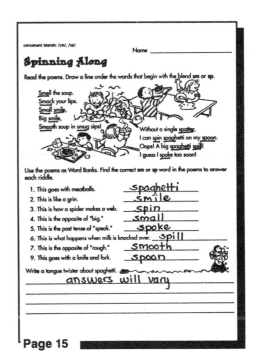

Use the poems as Word Banks. Find the correct sm or sp word in the poems to answer each riddle.

1. This goes with meatballs. __spaghetti__
2. This is like a grin. __smile__
3. This is how a spider makes a web. __spin__
4. This is the opposite of "big." __small__
5. This is the past tense of "speak." __spoke__
6. This is what happens when milk is knocked over. __spill__
7. This is the opposite of "rough." __smooth__
9. This goes with a knife and fork. __spoon__

Write a tongue twister about spaghetti. _____
__answers will vary__

---

consonant blends: /sn/, /sc/

Name _____

Scarecrows and Snails

Read the poems. Draw a line under the words that begin with the blend sc or sn.

The scarecrow
Has a scary scarf
To scare the crows away.
Scoot! Scat!
Scatter, crows!
Scoot and stay away!

Snake and Snail
Sniffed the snow,
Which muffled their snuffle attack.
Snake sneezed!
Snail sneezed!
Snow was on their backs!

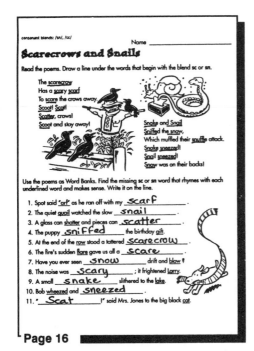

Use the poems as Word Banks. Find the missing sc or sn word that rhymes with each underlined word and makes sense. Write it on the line.

1. Spot said "arf" as he ran off with my __scarf__
2. The quiet quail watched the slow __snail__
3. A glass can shatter and pieces can __scatter__
4. The puppy __sniffed__ the birthday gift.
5. At the end of the row stood a tattered __scarecrow__
6. The fire's sudden flare gave us all a __scare__
7. Have you ever seen __snow__ drift and blow ?
8. The noise was __scary__; it frightened Larry.
9. A small __snake__ slithered to the lake.
10. Bob wheezed and __sneezed__
11. "__Scat__!" said Mrs. Jones to the big black cat.

---

consonant blends: /sw/, /tw/

Name _____

Swirl and Twirl

Write the blend sw on the lines to complete the words in the poem. Read the poem.

A _sw_imming _sw_an
Is _sw_ift and _sw_eet,
So _sw_eet it _sw_eeps me
Off my feet!

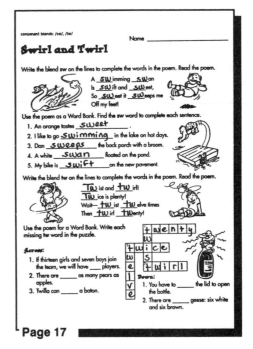

Use the poem as a Word Bank. Find the sw word to complete each sentence.
1. An orange tastes __sweet__
2. I like to go __swimming__ in the lake on hot days.
3. Dan __sweeps__ the back porch with a broom.
4. A white __swan__ floated on the pond.
5. My bike is __swift__ on the new pavement.

Write the blend tw on the lines to complete the words in the poem. Read the poem.

_Tw_ist and _tw_irl!
_Tw_ice is plenty!
Wait— _tw_ist _tw_elve times
Then _tw_irl _tw_enty!

Use the poem for a Word Bank. Write each missing tw word in the puzzle.

Across:
1. If thirteen girls and seven boys join the team, we will have ____ players.
2. There are ____ as many pears as apples.
3. Twilla can ____ a baton.

Down:
1. You have to ____ the lid to open the bottle.
2. There are ____ geese: six white and six brown.

Puzzle answers: twenty, twice, twirl, twelve, twist

IF87103 "Fun"damental Phonics

Page 18

consonant blend: /scr/

Name _____

Screeching Owl

Write the blend scr on the lines to complete the words in the poem. Read the poem.

A _scr_eeching owl
_Scr_atches on my _scr_een,
_Scr_aping for the food _scr_aps
It has seen.

Use the poem as a Word Bank. Find the correct scr word to answer each clue.

1. This is what the screeching owl scratches. — screen
2. The screeching owl scratches the screen to get these. — scraps
3. This is the sound the owl makes while scratching the screen. — screeching
4. The screeching owl is doing this to get food scraps. — scraping
5. This is what the screeching owl does to the screen. — scratches

Word Bank

scream   scramble   scrub
script   scroll   scribble

Read the sentences. Find the missing word in the Word Bank and write it on the line.

1. Bob wants to _scramble_ some eggs for breakfast.
2. Mr. Hernandez unrolled the _scroll_ to read the names of the top students.
3. Please write neatly; don't _scribble_ !
4. We had to use a brush to _scrub_ the stain off the floor.
5. Carl and Chung wrote the _script_ for the class play.
6. Everyone heard Beth _scream_ when she saw the alligator.

Page 19

consonant blend: /spl/

Name _____

Splashing Fish

Read the poem. Draw a line under the words that begin with the blend spl.

Splash!
Splish!
I hear fish!

Write a rhyming title for the poem.

_____ answers will vary _____

Word Bank

split   splurge   splinter   splat
splatter   splendid   splash   splint

Find the missing word in the Word Bank that rhymes with the underlined word and makes sense in the sentence. Write the word on the line.

1. Carry the platter carefully so you will not _splatter_ the gravy.
2. Morgan made a bid on the _splendid_ picture.
3. When Maria's finger hurt, it was the first hint that she needed a _splint_ .
4. We can each have a little bit if we _split_ the cookie.
5. This winter, I fell against a tree and got a _splinter_ .
6. After a quick dash, Lee jumped into the pool with a _splash_ !
7. May suddenly had the urge to _splurge_ on a new pair of shoes.
8. "_Splat_ !" went the cupcakes on the mat.

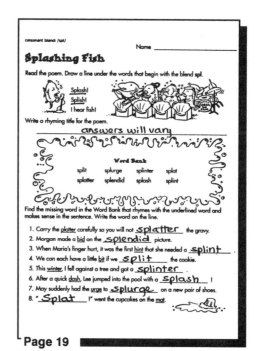

Page 20

consonant blend: /spr/

Name _____

Spring Has Sprung

Write the blend spr on the lines to complete the words in the poem and the Word Bank.
Read the poem.

_Spr_ing has _spr_ung!
_Spr_ing has _spr_ead!
A _spr_ay is _spr_inkling
My flower bed!

Word Bank

spree   sprain   spry
springy   sprang   sprout
sprinkler   sprint   sprawl

Use the poem as a Word Bank. Find the correct spr word in the poem to answer each riddle.

1. I come after winter. — spring
2. I am a fine jet of water. — spray
3. I am how you keep grass green. — sprinkling
4. I am what you do with butter. — spread

Find each missing word in the Word Bank to complete each sentence and write it in the puzzle.

Across:
3. Dad went on a shopping _____ at the hardware.
4. That rubber ball is so _____ that it bounces everywhere.
5. Soon the plants will _____ leaves.
6. The kitten _____ out of the box and ran off.
7. Juan and Peter _____ on the floor when they draw.
8. Be careful not to _____ your ankle.

Down:
1. Meg will _____ around the track twice.
2. That old dog is quite _____ .
3. Please move the _____ to water the roses.

Page 21

consonant blend: /squ/

Name _____

Squirrel Square

Write the blend squ on the lines to complete the words in the poem. Read the poem.

In _Squ_irrel _Squ_are,
The _squ_irrels there
_Squ_eak and _squ_awk,
_Squ_eal and talk!

Use the poem as a Word Bank. Find the correct squ words to complete each sentence and then write them in the puzzle.

Across:
2. The mouse gave a _____ and ran into the hole.
3. A shape with four equal sides is a _____ .
4. That gray _____ ate all our bird seed!

Down:
1. The plump piglet let out a _____ when he couldn't find his mother.
3. That _____ was made by a hawk.

Word Bank

squint   squirt   squishy
squeeze   squash   squad

Find the missing squ word in the Word Bank to complete each sentence.

1. Carla and Maria tried out for the cheerleading _squad_ .
2. Mark helped _squeeze_ oranges for fresh juice.
3. We had to _squint_ as we walked into the sunlight.
4. Many people like baked _squash_ on Thanksgiving.
5. I want to _squirt_ some mustard on my hot dog.
6. Bob doesn't like to hold worms because they feel _squishy_ .

IF87103 "Fun"damental Phonics

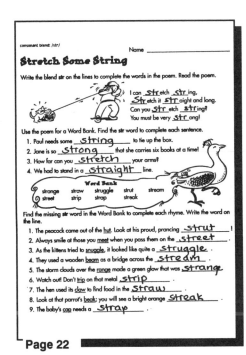

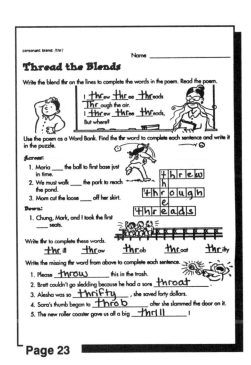

Page 22

consonant blend: /str/

Stretch Some String

Name _____

Write the blend str on the lines to complete the words in the poem. Read the poem.

I can _str_etch _str_ing,
_Str_etch it _str_aight and long.
Can you _str_etch _str_ing?
You must be very _str_ong!

Use the poem for a Word Bank. Find the str word to complete each sentence.
1. Paul needs some _string_ to tie up the box.
2. Jane is so _strong_ that she carries six books at a time!
3. How far can you _stretch_ your arms?
4. We had to stand in a _straight_ line.

Word Bank
strange   straw   struggle   strut   stream
street   strip   strap   streak

Find the missing str word in the Word Bank to complete each rhyme. Write the word on the line.
1. The peacock came out of the hut. Look at his proud, prancing _strut_ !
2. Always smile at those you meet when you pass them on the _street_ .
3. As the kittens tried to snuggle, it looked like quite a _struggle_ .
4. They used a wooden beam as a bridge across the _stream_ .
5. The storm clouds over the range made a green glow that was _strange_ .
6. Watch out! Don't trip on that metal _strip_ .
7. The hen used its claw to find food in the _straw_ .
8. Look at that parrot's beak; you will see a bright orange _streak_ .
9. The baby's cap needs a _strap_ .

Page 23

consonant blend: /thr/

Thread the Blends

Name _____

Write the blend thr on the lines to complete the words in the poem. Read the poem.

I _thr_ew _thr_ee _thr_eads
_Thr_ough the air.
I _thr_ew _thr_ee _thr_eads,
But where?

Use the poem as a Word Bank. Find the thr word to complete each sentence and write it in the puzzle.

Across:
1. Maria ____ the ball to first base just in time.
2. We must walk ____ the park to reach the pond.
3. Mom cut the loose ____ off her skirt.

Down:
1. Chung, Mark, and I took the first ____ seats.

t h r e w
h
t h r o u g h
r
e
t h r e a d s

Write thr to complete these words.
_thr_ill   _thr_ow   _thr_ob   _thr_oat   _thr_ifty

Write the missing thr word from above to complete each sentence.
1. Please _throw_ this in the trash.
2. Brett couldn't go sledding because he had a sore _throat_ .
3. Alesha was so _thrifty_ , she saved forty dollars.
4. Sara's thumb began to _throb_ after she slammed the door on it.
5. The new roller coaster gave us all a big _thrill_ !

Page 24

consonant digraph: /ch/

Choose Your Cake

Name _____

Write the blend ch on the lines to complete the words in the poem. Read the poem.

I _ch_oose the cake
I _ch_ew with ease.
_Ch_ocolate _ch_ip
_Ch_erry _ch_eese!

My _ch_eerful _ch_oice
Is one _ch_unk, please,
Of _ch_ocolate _ch_ip
_Ch_erry _ch_eese!

Use the poem as a Word Bank. Find the ch word to complete each sentence and write it in the puzzle.

Across:
5. The cake was iced with rich, dark ____.
6. Please put a sweet, red ____ on top of the sundae.
7. Sam wants a big ____ of cake.

Down:
1. Which kind of cheesecake would you ____?
2. My ____ would be a piece of cherry cheesecake.
3. We sprinkle ____ on top of pizza.
4. Everyone at the party was very ____.
5. Cheesecake is easy to ____.
6. Here's a chocolate ____ left over from the cookies.

c h   c h
h   h
c h o c o l a t e
o   c h e e s e
s   e
e   e
c h e r r y
c h i p   f
c h u n k

Page 25

consonant digraph: /sh/

Share a Wish

Name _____

Write the digraph sh on the lines to complete the words in the poems. Read the poems.

I _sh_all not _sh_out,
I _sh_all not _sh_ove,
I'll _sh_ine my _sh_oes
And _sh_ are my love!

Each and every fi_sh_,
Has the same wi_sh_:
To swi_sh_ in the water and
Not be on a di_sh_ !

Use the poems as Word Banks. Choose the correct sh word to answer the riddles.
1. This is a call.   _shout_
2. This is a hope.   _wish_
3. To move with a hissing sound.   _swish_
4. This is a plate or bowl.   _dish_
5. To do this is most thoughtful.   _share_
6. This is the sun's job.   _shine_
7. This means "to push past."   _shove_
8. These go on your feet.   _shoes_
9. This swims in seas and lakes.   _Fish_

What will you wish for on your next birthday?
answers will vary

111

© Instructional Fair • TS Denison

IF87103 "Fun"damental Phonics

consonant digraph: /th/

These Teeth

Name _____

Write the digraph th on the lines to complete the words in the poems. Read the poems.

Th ese are ours,
Th ose are th eirs.
Through th is and
th at,
The whole group shares!

The tee th
In your mou th
Grow nor th
And sou th !
Th at's the tru th
For every too th !

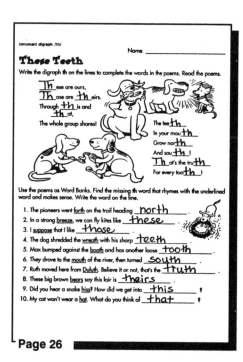

Use the poems as Word Banks. Find the missing th word that rhymes with the underlined word and makes sense. Write the word on the line.

1. The pioneers went forth on the trail heading _north_
2. In a strong breeze, we can fly kites like _these_
3. I suppose that I like _those_
4. The dog shredded the wreath with his sharp _teeth_
5. Max bumped against the booth and has another loose _tooth_
6. They drove to the mouth of the river, then turned _south_
7. Ruth moved here from Duluth. Believe it or not, that's the _truth_
8. These big brown bears say this lair is _theirs_
9. Did you hear a snake hiss? How did we get into _this_ ?
10. My cat won't wear a hat. What do you think of _that_ ?

Page 26

---

consonant digraph: /wh/

Whisper

Name _____

Write the digraph wh on the lines to complete the words in the poem. Read the poem.

Wh isper your questions,
Wh isper and share:
" Wh ich?" " Wh en?"

" Wh at?" " Wh y?"
" Wh ere?"

Write sentences using each wh word in the poem.
1. _answers will vary_
2. _____
3. _____
4. _____
5. _____
6. _____

Write wh to complete these words.

| wh ittle | wh eelchair | wh ether |
| Wh ile | wh imper | wh iskers |

Read the sentences. Write the missing word on the line.
1. Do you know _whether_ we are going swimming or hiking?
2. Megan sat in a _wheelchair_ as she waited for the doctor to check her leg.
3. The cat's _whiskers_ twitched as it watched the bird.
4. Uncle Van can _whittle_ a piece of wood into a beautiful carving.
5. We heard the puppy _whimper_ at night.
6. Maria played in a soccer game _while_ her brother played in a baseball game.

Page 27

---

consonant digraph: /ph/

Phone an Elephant

Name _____

Write the digraph ph on the lines to complete the words in the poems. Read the poems.

Ele ph ant, ele ph ant
Is so alone.
I'll send him a ph oto
And call him by ph one!

Autogra ph !
Photogra ph !
Phonogra ph , too.
I have every kind of gra ph
How about you?

Use the poems as Word Banks. Find the correct word to answer each riddle.
1. This is what you use to call the lonely elephant. _phone_
2. This plays records. _phonograph_
3. This kind of chart compares things. _graph_
4. This animal is all alone in the poem. _elephant_
5. This is what a famous person writes on his or her picture. _autograph_
6. You need a camera to take one of these. _photograph_ (or photo)

Write ph to complete these words.
ph easant   paragra ph   ph onics   telegra ph

Read the sentences. Write the missing word on the line.
1. Write a _paragraph_ about thunderstorms.
2. Use _phonics_ to help you sound out new words.
3. A _pheasant_ landed in the field near the lake.
4. Morse Code was invented to send messages over _telegraph_ wires.

Page 28

---

consonant digraph: /gh/

Enough!

Name _____

Write the digraph gh on the lines to complete the words in the poem. Read the poem.

Cou gh enough
And it feels rou gh !
Lau gh enough
And life won't feel tou gh !

Use the poem as a Word Bank. Find the gh word to complete each sentence.
1. We need to sand this board because it is too _rough_
2. The clown made us all _laugh_
3. The steak was too _tough_ to cut.
4. Our class earned _enough_ money to go on a field trip.
5. The smoke from the campfire made us all _cough_

Write a rhyming poem about something that makes you laugh.
answers will vary
_____
_____
_____
_____

Draw a picture to go with your poem.
Student may also draw on reverse side.

Page 29

    IF87103 "Fun"damental Phonics

On the Knoll

Name _____

Write kn on the lines to complete the words in the Word Bank.

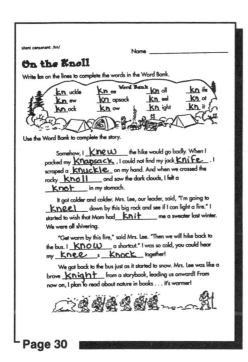

Word Bank

kn uckle   kn ee   kn oll   kn ife
kn ew   kn apsack   kn eel   kn ot
kn ock   kn ow   kn ight   kn it

Use the Word Bank to complete the story.

Somehow, I __knew__ the hike would go badly. When I packed my __knapsack__, I could not find my jack __knife__. I scraped a __knuckle__ on my hand. And when we crossed the rocky __knoll__ and saw the dark clouds, I felt a __knot__ in my stomach.

It got colder and colder. Mrs. Lee, our leader, said, "I'm going to __kneel__ down by this big rock and see if I can light a fire." I started to wish that Mom had __knit__ me a sweater last winter. We were all shivering.

"Get warm by this fire," said Mrs. Lee. "Then we will hike back to the bus. I __know__ a shortcut." I was so cold, you could hear my __knee__ s __knock__ together!

We got back to the bus just as it started to snow. Mrs. Lee was like a brave __knight__ from a storybook, leading us onward! From now on, I plan to read about nature in books . . . it's warmer!

What Did I Write?

Name _____

Write wr on the lines to complete the words in the poem. Read the poem.

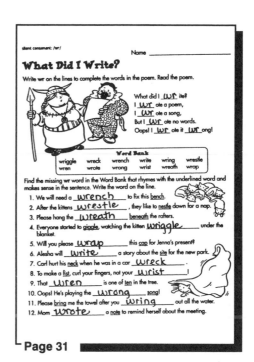

What did I __wr__ ite?
I __wr__ ote a poem,
I __wr__ ote a song,
But I __wr__ ote no words.
Oops! I __wr__ ote it __wr__ ong!

Word Bank

wriggle   wreck   wrench   write   wring   wrestle
wren   wrote   wrong   wrist   wreath   wrap

Find the missing wr word in the Word Bank that rhymes with the underlined word and makes sense in the sentence. Write the word on the line.

1. We will need a __wrench__ to fix this bench.
2. After the kittens __wrestle__, they like to nestle down for a nap.
3. Please hang the __wreath__ beneath the rafters.
4. Everyone started to giggle, watching the kitten __wriggle__ under the blanket.
5. Will you please __wrap__ this cap for Jenna's present?
6. Alesha will __write__ a story about the site for the new park.
7. Carl hurt his neck when he was in a car __wreck__.
8. To make a fist, curl your fingers, not your __wrist__.
9. That __wren__ is one of ten in the tree.
10. Oops! He's playing the __wrong__ song!
11. Please bring me the towel after you __wring__ out all the water.
12. Mom __wrote__ a note to remind herself about the meeting.

Such a Sight!

Name _____

Write gh on the lines to complete the words in the poem. Read the poem.

When the sun is bri __gh__ t,
And the clouds are li __gh__ t,
And the birds take fli __gh__ t,
It's a beautiful si __gh__ t!
But beware! At ni __gh__ t,
It may cause fri __gh__ t,
When two cats fi __gh__ t,
(Well, they mi __gh__ t!)
Am I wrong or am I ri __gh__ t?

Use the poem as a Word Bank. Use the gh words in the poem to complete the story.

One dark __night__, we sat around a campfire. The campfire was warm and __bright__. The __light__ from the flames cast shadows on our tents. We thought it __might__ be fun to tell scary stories. Ted told an eerie story that gave everyone a __fright__. Ted and Mark started to __fight__ about the ending of the story. Just then, an owl took __flight__ from a tree. It made us all jump up! It was quite a __sight__ as the owl swooped over our heads. After this last scare, we decided this was the __right__ time to go to bed!

Write a poem about night.

__answers will vary__
_____
_____
_____

Gnats and Gnus

Name _____

Write gn on the lines to complete the words in the poem. Read the poem.

A __gn__ at sat
Upon a __gn__ u.
The __gn__ at said,
"__Gn__ ow are you?"

Write a tongue twister about a gnat and a gnu.

__answers will vary__

Word Bank

assign   gnarled   lasagna   sign   gnat
resign   campaign   design   gnaw   gnome

Find the gn word in the Word Bank to answer each riddle.

1. This means "to quit."   __resign__
2. This is noodles, cheese, and sauce.   __lasagna__
3. This is a tiny bug.   __gnat__
4. This is a make-believe little man.   __gnome__
5. This is when something's twisted.   __gnarled__
6. This is when something is given to you to do.   __assign__
7. This shows you which way to go.   __sign__
8. This is a pattern to make something.   __design__
9. This is a time when people hear speeches and debates.   __campaign__
10. This means "to chew hard."   __gnaw__

IF87103 "Fun"damental Phonics

Page 34

Name _____

Little Lamb

Write mb on the line to complete the words in the poem. Read the poem.

Poor little la **mb** ,
You can't cli **mb** a tree li **mb**
Or wiggle your thu **mb**
Or co **mb** your wooly hair.
But, don't fret, little la **mb** ,
You can give us wool—
So there!

Use the poem as a Word Bank. Find the mb word to answer each question.

1. Who will grow up to be a sheep? — lamb
2. What goes together with brush? — comb
3. What is another word for branch? — limb
4. What do you do to go up? — climb
5. What goes along with four fingers? — thumb

Find the mb words in the Word Bank to complete each sentence and write it in the puzzle.

Across:
1. The squirrel will ____ to the top of the tree for an acorn.
3. Hold the pen between your fingers and your ____.
4. The tiny ____ wobbled as it walked in the pasture.
5. Matt's hands were so cold that they were ____.

Down:
1. Maria likes to ____ her little sister's hair.
2. The dog licked up every ____ that fell on the floor.
4. A robin built a nest on a ____ of the oak tree.

(crossword puzzle: climb, thumb, lamb, numb, comb, crumb, limb)

Word Bank
comb   limb   lamb   climb
crumb   thumb   numb

Page 35

Name _____

Pitch and Catch

Write tch on the lines to complete the words in the poem. Read the poem.

I'll pi **tch** ,
You'll ca **tch** !
Wa **tch** the ball!
Nice stre **tch** !
Good ca **tch** !
Now, let's swi **tch** !

Use the poem as a Word Bank. Find the correct tch words to complete each sentence and write it in the puzzle.

Across:
4. Everyone will ____ the movie.
5. Pedro had to ____ out his arm to tag Max.

Down:
1. Can you ____ a fly ball?
2. We ____ places after the third "out."
3. Bill likes to ____ fastballs.

(crossword puzzle: watch, catch, stretch, switch, pitch)

Read the sentences. Find the missing word in the Word Bank and write it on the line.

Word Bank fetch   scratch   ditch   batch   sketch   stitch

1. Rain flooded the ditch with water.
2. Let's bake a big batch of chocolate oatmeal cookies.
3. Morgan uses a pencil to sketch pictures of birds.
4. No matter how much it itches, never scratch an insect bite.
5. Dad will stitch my new merit badge on my uniform.
6. My dog likes to fetch the ball from the lake.

Page 36

Name _____

Nice and Cozy

Read the poems. Draw a line under the words containing the letter c. Listen to the sound the letter c makes in each word.

I'd like some rice,
And a pizza slice
With twice the spice,
And apple juice with ice.
So, what's the price?
That's nice!

The cute cuddly cat
Curled up on the mat,
All cozy and fat,
A comfortable cat!

Read each clue. Find the correct word in the poems and write it on the line.

1. This is how much spice I want on my pizza slice. — twice
2. I want my juice to have this in it. — ice
3. The cute cuddly cat did this on a mat. — curled
4. I want some of this with my pizza slice and juice. — rice
5. I thought this about the price. — nice
6. I want this much pizza with twice the spice. — a slice
7. I want ice in this. — juice
8. He is cute, cuddly, and curled on a mat. — cat
9. I want twice as much of this on my pizza slice. — spice
10. I asked about this so that I would know the cost of my food. — price

Write a sentence describing how to eat a slice of pizza.

answers will vary

Page 37

Name _____

On Stage

Read the poem. Draw a line under the words containing the letter g. Listen to the sound the g makes.

When that bird was your age,
She left her golden cage,
Got to dance on the stage,
And made the front page!

Read the clues. Find the missing word in the poem and write it in the puzzle.

Across:
3. The bird in the cage was your ____ when she became famous.
5. The bird danced on a ____.

Down:
1. The bird in the cage got to ____ on stage.
2. The bird that danced on stage lived in a ____.
4. The bird danced so well her picture was on the front ____.

(crossword puzzle: dance, cage, page, stage, age)

Read the sentences. Find the missing word in the Word Bank and write it on the line.

Word Bank engine   gym   garden   gentle   giant   sugar   ginger   goose

1. Beth planted cucumbers and beans in her garden
2. We are going to play basketball in the gym after school.
3. We need sugar to sweeten the iced tea.
4. The engine roared as the driver sped to the finish line.
5. A very tall person may seem like a giant to a baby.
6. Please be gentle when you hold the little kitten.
7. A honking goose waddled toward the pond.
8. Mom added some spicy ginger to the cookie batter.

On the Loose

Name _____

Read the poem. Draw a line under the words containing the letter s. Listen to the sound the letter s makes.

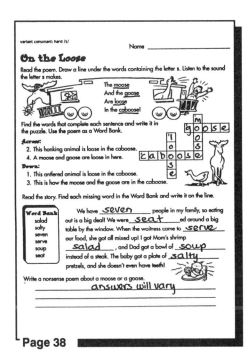

The moose
And the goose
Are loose
In the caboose!

Find the words that complete each sentence and write it in the puzzle. Use the poem as a Word Bank.

Across:
2. This honking animal is loose in the caboose.
4. A moose and goose are loose in here.

Down:
1. This antlered animal is loose in the caboose.
3. This is how the moose and the goose are in the caboose.

Puzzle answers: g o o s e (across 2), c a b o o s e (across 4), m o o s e (down 1), l o o s e (down 3)

Read the story. Find each missing word in the Word Bank and write it on the line.

Word Bank
salad
salty
seven
serve
soup
seat

We have _seven_ people in my family, so eating out is a big deal! We were _seat_ ed around a big table by the window. When the waitress came to _serve_ our food, she got all mixed up! I got Mom's shrimp _salad_, and Dad got a bowl of _soup_ instead of a steak. The baby got a plate of _salty_ pretzels, and she doesn't even have teeth!

Write a nonsense poem about a moose or a goose.
answers will vary

Page 38

What Rose Chose

Name _____

Read the poem. Listen for the sound the letter s makes.

Rose chose
To point the nose
Of the hose
On every rose.
She sprayed these and those,
And all the rest, I suppose!

Read the clues. Find the correct word in the poem and write it on the line.

1. This is the part of the hose that was pointed at every rose. _nose_
2. This is who chose to point the hose on every rose. _Rose_
3. The roses Rose chose to spray. _these_ and _those_
4. Rose chose to point the nose of this at every rose. _hose_
5. Rose pointed the hose at every one of these. _rose_
6. Rose did this when she started watering each rose. _chose_

Read the sentences. Find the missing word in the Word Bank and write it on the line.

Word Bank please   cans   cheese   his   eyes

1. I knew this was the right puppy when he looked at me with his big brown _eyes_.
2. We need twenty-four _cans_ of soda pop for the picnic.
3. May we _please_ have more potato chips?
4. Gretchen ordered a pizza with extra _cheese_ on it.
5. Carl searched but could not find _his_ homework.

Write a tongue twister about a rose.
answers will vary

Page 39

Applause Please

Name _____

Write au on the lines to complete the words in the poem. Read the poem.

After _Au_gust,
There's a p_au_se
Then it's _au_tumn
Appl_au_se, appl_au_se!
Why?
Bec_au_se!

Read the clues. Find the missing word in the poem and write it in the puzzle.

Across:
2. The season after summer is ____.
3. The performance received loud ____.
5. She was late ____ she overslept.

Down:
1. ____ is a summer month.
4. There was a ____ before the next act.

Puzzle answers: a u t u m n (across 2), a p p l a u s e (across 3), b e c a u s e (across 5), A (down 1, august), p a u s e (down 4)

Find the missing au word in the Word Bank that rhymes with the underlined word and makes sense in the sentence. Write the word on the line.

Word Bank haunted   somersault   cause   vault   haul

1. It's not my fault that we can't open the _vault_.
2. Sam taunted me for being afraid to go into the _haunted_ house.
3. Paul said he would be happy to _haul_ the wood for us.
4. When Dad said I could have a malt, I felt like doing a _somersault_!
5. Do you know the _cause_ of this long pause?

Page 40

Mouse Law

Name _____

Write aw on the lines to complete the words in the poem. Read the poem.

The mouse started to gn_aw_
On the hay and the str_aw_,
But then he made a face.
He said, "There is a mouse l_aw_:
Never eat r_aw_ str_aw_,
Is there an oven in this place?"

Use the poem as a Word Bank. Find the correct aw word to answer each clue.

1. The mouse started to do this to the food. _gnaw_
2. The mouse asked for an oven because he never ate food that was ___. _raw_
3. The mouse was eating hay and this. _straw_
4. The mouse wouldn't eat raw food because of this. _law_

Read the story. Find the missing aw word in the Word Bank to complete each sentence.

The first day at the cabin, I woke up at _dawn_ with a huge, sleepy _yawn_. There was dew on the _lawn_ that rolled down to the lake. I heard a sharp cry, and saw a _hawk_ in the sky. His _claws_ were sharp, and his wings were spread wide. As he flew away, a baby _fawn_ came silently out of the woods. She nibbled some clover. I stood very still so I would not scare her. We both enjoyed the peaceful morning at the cabin.

Word Bank
hawk
lawn
yawn
dawn
fawn
claws

Page 41

115

After Breakfast

Name _____

Write ea on the line to complete the words in the poem. Read the poem.

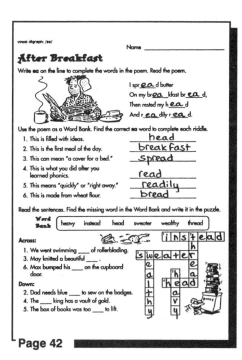

I spr **ea** d butter
On my br **ea** kfast br **ea** d,
Then rested my h **ea** d
And r **ea** dily r **ea** d.

Use the poem as a Word Bank. Find the correct ea word to complete each riddle.

1. This is filled with ideas. **head**
2. This is the first meal of the day. **breakfast**
3. This can mean "a cover for a bed." **spread**
4. This is what you did after you learned phonics. **read**
5. This means "quickly" or "right away." **readily**
6. This is made from wheat flour. **bread**

Read the sentences. Find the missing word in the Word Bank and write it in the puzzle.

Word Bank: heavy   instead   head   sweater   wealthy   thread

Across:
1. We went swimming ____ of rollerblading.
3. May knitted a beautiful ____ .
6. Max bumped his ____ on the cupboard door.

Down:
2. Dad needs blue ____ to sew on the badges.
4. The ____ king has a vault of gold.
5. The box of books was too ____ to lift.

Puzzle answers: ¹instead, ²sweater, ⁵head, (down) wealthy, heavy, thread

Page 42

Eight Reindeer

Name _____

Write ei on the lines to complete the words in the poem. Read the poem.

Ei ght r **ei** ndeer
Pulled a sl **ei** gh
In my n **ei** ghborhood today
Ei ght r **ei** ndeer
Pulled their w **ei** ght.
I grabbed the r **ei** ns
To guide the fr **ei** ght!

Use the poem as a Word Bank. Find the ei word in the poem to answer each clue.

1. This is where eight reindeer came today. **neighborhood**
2. This is what the eight reindeer pulled. **sleigh**
3. Each of the eight reindeer pulled their own of this. **weight**
4. This is the part of the sleigh I grabbed. **reins**
5. Eight of these came to my neighborhood today. **reindeer**
6. This is what I guided when I grabbed the sleigh reins. **Freight**
7. This is the number of reindeer that pulled the sleigh. **eight**

Use the poem as a Word Bank. Find the missing ei word to complete each sentence of the story.

When we awoke, we found our whole **neighborhood** covered with fresh snow. **Eight** of us put on warm clothes and rushed outside to build a snowman. We all had to help push the snowballs because of their heavy **weight** . Meish made a snow sculpture of a **reindeer** with antlers. Carla used ropes to make a harness and **reins** . The snow sculpture made everyone want to go for a **sleigh** ride. Mr. Snowdon said that all of us at one time would be too much **freight** for his horse to pull. So we took turns. It was a great snow day!

Page 43

Have a Piece

Name _____

Write ie on the lines to complete the words in the Word Bank.

sh **ie** ld   rel **ie** f   gr **ie** f   p **ie** ce   f **ie** ld   shr **ie** k   br **ie** f   bel **ie** ve   ach **ie** ve   th **ie** f   ch **ie** f

Use the Word Bank to help you find the missing ie word and write it on the line.

1. Alesha gave a sigh of **relief** when she found her kitten.
2. Sara's **grief** when her friend moved away made me sad, too.
3. Do you really **believe** that some day we will fly to another planet?
4. Mrs. Ramirez said we could each have one **piece** of candy.
5. Ahmed gave a **brief** , five-minute report about the book he read.
6. Long ago a knight used a **shield** to protect himself.
7. The crowd gave a **shriek** when the loud firework exploded.
8. Mr. Edwards is the new **chief** of the fire department.
9. Greg worked hard to **achieve** the award.
10. Chung and Carl watched the colts run in the open **field** .
11. Ms. Waters was upset when a **thief** took her necklace.

Write a three-line rhyming poem about something you believe.
answers will vary
_____
_____

Page 44

Coast to Coast

Name _____

Write oa on the lines to complete the words in the poem. Read the poem.

I don't like to b **oa** st
But I travel in style.
I fly to the c **oa** st
But we stop every mile
To have slices of r **oa** st
Or some tea from the Nile,
Served with unbuttered t **oa** st
Made by crocodiles!

Use the poem as a Word Bank. Find the correct oa word to answer each riddle.

1. This is "to cook slowly in the oven." **roast**
2. This is the border by the sea. **coast**
3. This is a bragging statement. **boast**
4. This is what we serve with tea! **toast**

Write oa on the lines to complete the Word Bank. Then read the poems and write the missing words from the Word Bank on the lines.

Word Bank: b **oa** t   thr **oa** t   g **oa** t   c **oa** t   fl **oa** t

A silly **goat**
Jumped off a **boat**
To swim and **float**
He had no **coat**
So he got a sore **throat** !

On the back of this paper, draw a picture to show what happened in one of the poems.

Page 45

IF87103 "Fun"damental Phonics

Loud Cloud

Name _____

Write ou on the lines to complete the words in the poem and the Word Bank. Read the poem.

Oh, so l_ou_d!
Above my h_ou_se,
A rainy d_ou_d
Was as gray as a m_ou_se
The thunder was so pr_ou_d
Of that lovely gray d_ou_d
That it clapped right out l_ou_d!

Word Bank

m_ou_ntain
c_ou_ch   b_ou_nce
f_ou_nd   ab_ou_t

Use the poem and the Word Bank to find the ou words to complete the story.

We decided to drive to a ski lodge on our vacation. As we drove into the hills, we could see that the peak was covered with a low, gray _cloud_ . The road leading up the _mountain_ was very bumpy. Every time we ran over a pothole, the car would _bounce_ . The tires rumbled _loud_ ly on the rocky road. The misty cloud made it hard to see. We almost turned back and went back home!

We drove for two hours on that bad road. But then, we reached the ski lodge, a log _house_ with a steep roof and a stone chimney. We were over-joyed to get here! We _found_ our rooms, unpacked and then skied all afternoon. The owner of the lodge was very _proud_ of the fine, old place and told us all _about_ its history at dinner. That night, we sat on the overstuffed _couch_ in front of the fireplace. We told ghost stories and popped popcorn. We were glad we had made it to the mountaintop!

Boil and Broil

Name _____

Read the poem. Draw a line under the words that contain oi.

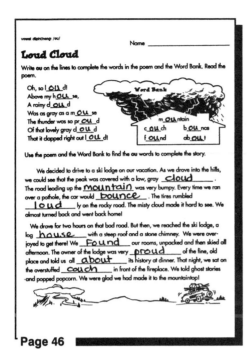

First let it boil,
Then add the oil.
Now wrap it in foil.
Next, let it broil.
Don't let it spoil,
Or drop it in the soil!

Use the poem as a Word Bank. Find the oi word to answer each clue.

1. This is what you add after boiling.   _add oil_
2. Be sure you don't drop it in this!   _soil_
3. After you wrap it, the recipe says to do this.   _broil_
4. This is what you must use to wrap it.   _foil_
5. This recipe says that you must do this first.   _boil_

Write oi on the lines to complete the words. Use the Word Bank to find each oi word and write it in the puzzle.

Word Bank

c_oi_n   ch_oi_ce   j_oi_n   v_oi_ce
p_oi_nt   n_oi_se   m_oi_st

Across:
3. Add just enough water to make the batter ___ .
4. Dial the phone after you put in a ___ .
5. Ling will ___ us at the park.
6. Dad's ___ is so loud, it can be heard for blocks!

Down:
1. Do you hear a squeaky ___ ?
2. My pencil ___ broke.
4. Make a ___ between a hamburger or a hot dog.

Puzzle answers:
n o i s e
m o i s t
c o i n
h
j o i n
v o i c e

Enjoy!

Name _____

Write oy on the lines to complete the words in the poem and the Word Bank. Read the poem and the words.

Oh, b_oy_!
Oh, j_oy_!
A new t_oy_!

Word Bank

r_oy_al   ann_oy_
cowb_oy_   destr_oy_
l_oy_al   _oy_sters
v_oy_age   ah_oy_

Use the poem and the Word Bank. Find the oy word to complete each sentence in the story.

When my great-grandfather was a young _boy_ , he went on a sea _voyage_ . He loved to talk about that trip. He met many famous people on the huge ship, including a _cowboy_ from a Wild West show and a _royal_ princess.

My great-grandfather's greatest _joy_ was to run very fast and then slide across the deck. He would shout, "_Ahoy_ there!" to warn people to get out of the way. Although this would _annoy_ the adults, nothing could _destroy_ my great-grandfather's delight in doing this.

He had other memories, too. His father bought him a _toy_ ship at one of the shops on board. One night at dinner, he was served a big plate of _oysters_ by mistake! When the trip was over, he would often play sea captain, with his _loyal_ dog Banjo as his first mate.

Write a riddle about a toy you enjoy.

answers will vary

Unknown

Name _____

Write ow on the lines to complete the words in the Word Bank.

r_ow_   cr_ow_   rainb_ow_   gl_ow_s
mead_ow_   _ow_n   bl_ow_   sh_ow_
sn_ow_   gr_ow_   bl_ow_n   fl_ow_
yell_ow_   unkn_ow_n

Read each poem. Find the ow words in the Word Bank and write them on the lines. Then in the box beside each poem, draw a picture to go along with the poem.

The sun gl_ow_s
And melts the sn_ow_ .
Roosters cr_ow_ ,
Breezes bl_ow_ ,
Flowers gr_ow_
All in a r_ow_ !

The wind has bl_ow_n
The hat that I _ow_n ,
And now it's fl_ow_n
To a place unkn_ow_n!

In nature there is no sh_ow_
As beautiful as a rainb_ow_ .
Its curve glows with red and yell_ow_
As it reaches across the green mead_ow_

117

IF87103 "Fun"damental Phonics

Take a Bow

Name _____

Read the poem. Draw a line under each word that rhymes with how.

All you farmers, take a <u>bow</u>!
We'd like to thank you for our <u>chow</u>,
For <u>how</u> you rise to milk each <u>cow</u>,
Then feed the piglets with the <u>sow</u>,
And *then* go in the fields to <u>plow</u>.
<u>Wow</u>! We <u>vow</u> to thank you <u>now</u>!

Use the poem as a Word Bank. Find the ow word to answer each riddle.

1. This means "not later."   now
2. This is a mother pig.   sow
3. This makes furrows in the soil. plow
4. This farm animal gives milk.   cow
5. This is a promise.   vow
6. This is bending from the waist. bow
7. This is another word for "food." chow
8. This means "in what way something is done." how

Write a four-line rhyming poem about something that would make you say "Wow!"
answers will vary

Page 50

A Few of the Crew

Name _____

Write ew on the lines to complete the words in the poem. Read the poem.

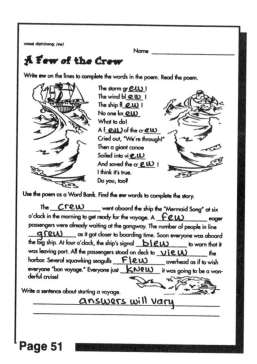

The storm gr ew !
The wind bl ew !
The ship fl ew !
No one kn ew
What to do!
A f ew of the cr ew
Cried out, "We're through!"
Then a giant canoe
Sailed into vi ew
And saved the cr ew !
I think it's true.
Do you, too?

Use the poem as a Word Bank. Find the ew words to complete the story.

The ___crew___ went aboard the ship the "Mermaid Song" at six o'clock in the morning to get ready for the voyage. A ___few___ eager passengers were already waiting at the gangway. The number of people in line ___grew___ as it got closer to boarding time. Soon everyone was aboard the big ship. At four o'clock, the ship's signal ___blew___ to warn that it was leaving port. All the passengers stood on deck to ___view___ the harbor. Several squawking seagulls ___flew___ overhead as if to wish everyone "bon voyage." Everyone just ___knew___ it was going to be a wonderful cruise!

Write a sentence about starting a voyage.
answers will vary

Page 51

My Special Jar

Name _____

Write ar on the lines to complete the words in the poem. Read the poem.

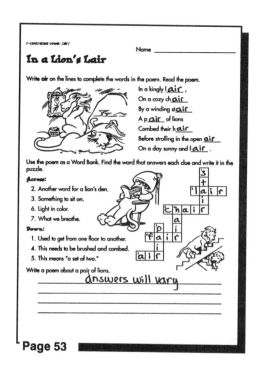

A toy c ar ,
A gold st ar ,
A sweet candy b ar ,
And a stange black stone
As smooth as t ar .
They are all in this j ar !
How's that so f ar ?

Use the poem as a Word Bank. Find the ar word in the poem to answer each riddle.

1. It means "the opposite of near."   far
2. A container to hold jam or jelly.   jar
3. At night, this twinkles in the dark sky. star
4. This is a kind of chocolate candy.   bar
5. This black mixture is used on roads.   tar
6. This is another word for automobile.   car

Write ar on the lines to complete the words in the Word Bank. Then read the poem and write the words where they belong.

If it's not too hard
Could you please guard
My baseball card
While I play in the yard ?

Word Bank
c ar d
gu ar d
y ar d
h ar d

Write a list of five things you would keep in a jar.
answers will vary

Page 52

In a Lion's Lair

Name _____

Write air on the lines to complete the words in the poem. Read the poem.

In a kingly l air ,
On a cozy ch air
By a winding st air
A p air of lions
Combed their h air
Before strolling in the open air
On a day sunny and f air .

Use the poem as a Word Bank. Find the word that answers each clue and write it in the puzzle.

Across:
2. Another word for a lion's den.
3. Something to sit on.
6. Light in color.
7. What we breathe.

Down:
1. Used to get from one floor to another.
4. This needs to be brushed and combed.
5. This means "a set of two."

Write a poem about a pair of lions.
answers will vary

Page 53

Page 54

Name _____

Do You Dare?

Write /are/ on the lines to complete the words in the poem. Read the poem.

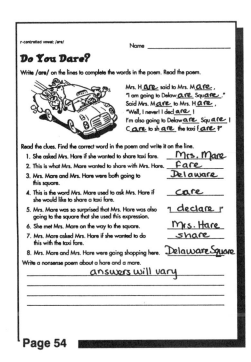

Mrs. H**are** said to Mrs. M**are**,
"I am going to Delaw**are** Square."
Said Mrs. M**are** to Mrs. H**are**,
"Well, I never! I decl**are** !
I'm also going to Delaw**are** Square. I
C**are** to sh**are** the taxi f**are** ?"

Read the clues. Find the correct word in the poem and write it on the line.

1. She asked Mrs. Hare if wanted to share taxi fare. **Mrs. Mare**
2. This is what Mrs. Mare wanted to share with Mrs. Hare. **fare**
3. Mrs. Mare and Mrs. Hare were both going to this square. **Delaware**
4. This is the word Mrs. Mare used to ask Mrs. Hare if she would like to share a taxi fare. **care**
5. Mrs. Mare was so surprised that Mrs. Hare was also going to the square that she used this expression. **"I declare !"**
6. She met Mrs. Mare on the way to the square. **Mrs. Hare**
7. Mrs. Mare asked Mrs. Hare if she wanted to do this with the taxi fare. **share**
8. Mrs. Mare and Mrs. Hare were going shopping here. **Delaware Square**

Write a nonsense poem about a hare and a mare.
answers will vary

Page 55

Name _____

Observe

Write er on the lines to complete the words in the poem. Read the poem

Trees we cons**er**ve,
Jams we pres**er**ve,
Treats we des**er**ve,
Seats we res**er**ve,
Rules we obs**er**ve,
And foods we s**er**ve!

Read the clues. Find the correct word in the poem and write it on the line.

1. When we make strawberries into jam, we do this. **preserve**
2. This means when we merit an award. **deserve**
3. We do this to bring food to the table. **serve**
4. We do this when we don't waste resources. **conserve**
5. We do this when we buy tickets for a concert. **reserve**
6. Everyone needs to do this with rules. **observe**

Write a rhyming poem about a treat you deserve. Include a description of the treat and why you deserve it.
answers will vary

Page 56

Name _____

Hear, Hear!

Write ear on the lines to complete the words in the poem. Read the poem.

H**ear**, h**ear** for the **ear** !
Your **ear** is d**ear** !
It lets you h**ear**
Both far and n**ear**

From y**ear** to y**ear**,
Never f**ear**
To praise each **ear** !
Is that cl**ear**?

Use the poem as a Word Bank. Find the ear word to complete each sentence and write it in the puzzle.

Across:
3. A rabbit's _____ is longer than a cat's.
5. Did you _____ a creaking noise?
6. Sheila lives _____ the library.

2. That locket is very _____ to Mia.
4. In what _____ was the first space shuttle launched?

Down:
1. The water is so _____ you can see the bottom.

Read the sentences. Find the missing ear word in the Word Bank and write it on the line. Then circle the words in the puzzle.

1. The driver put the car in high **gear** .
2. They will **shear** the sheep next week.
3. Please don't **smear** chalk all over the paper.
4. Cavemen could catch fish with a **spear** .
5. It is a long wait if you are at the **rear** of a line.

Word Bank
gear
smear
spear
shear
rear

Page 57

Name _____

Whirl Around

Write ir on the lines to complete the words in the poems. Read the poems. Then write a title on the line above each poem.

answers will vary
Flower g**ir**l,
How your flowers tw**ir**l,
And wh**ir**l, and sw**ir**l.

answers will vary
If you get d**ir**t,
On a sh**ir**t or a sk**ir**t,
Just take water
And squ**ir**t, squ**ir**t, squ**ir**t!

Read the sentences. Find the missing word in the poems and write it on the line.

1. Patrick planted seeds after he dug holes in the **dirt** .
2. We watched the water **swirl** around as it went down the drain.
3. May spilled lemonade all over her pleated **skirt** .
4. On a hot day, it is fun to **squirt** each other with water.
5. That new **girl** plays the piano very well.
6. A strong gust of wind made the leaves **whirl** up into the air.
7. Mark wore his new plaid **shirt** to the game.
8. Can you **twirl** a baton?

Read the words in the Word Bank. Write a sentence using each of the words.

Word Bank   circus   squirrel   firm   squirm

1. **answers will vary**
2. _____
3. _____
4. _____

IF87103 "Fun"damental Phonics

Page 58

Name _____

Picture This

Write ure on the lines to complete the words in the poem. Read the poem.

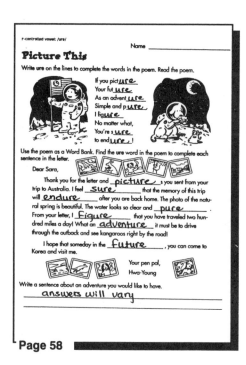

If you pict**ure**
Your fut**ure**
As an advent**ure**
Simple and p**ure**,
I fig**ure**
No matter what,
You're s**ure**
to end**ure**!

Use the poem as a Word Bank. Find the ure word in the poem to complete each sentence in the letter.

Dear Sara,

Thank you for the letter and **picture** s you sent from your trip to Australia. I feel **sure** that the memory of this trip will **endure** after you are back home. The photo of the natural spring is beautiful. The water looks so clear and **pure**. From your letter, I **figure** that you have traveled two hundred miles a day! What an **adventure** it must be to drive through the outback and see kangaroos right by the road!

I hope that someday in the **future**, you can come to Korea and visit me.

Your pen pal,
Hwa-Young

Write a sentence about an adventure you would like to have.

answers will vary

Page 58

Page 59

Name _____

An Underwater Adventure

Read the compound word. On the lines, write the two words that make up each compound word. Then use the compound words to complete the story.

1. seafood	sea food	7. seagull	sea gull
2. newspaper	news paper	8. toolbox	tool box
3. notebook	note book	9. underwater	under water
4. smokestack	smoke stack	10. seaweed	sea weed
5. boathouse	boat house	11. sunburn	sun burn
6. seashell	sea shell	12. starfish	star fish

Use the compound words from the list to complete the story.

Taro and Tori read an article in the **newspaper** about a ship that sank near their home. They called Uncle Ken. He told them to meet him at the **boathouse** where he kept his salvage boat.

They ran down the dock where people were selling shrimp and other **seafood**. Uncle Ken was packing his supplies. He always took his **toolbox** in case he needed to fix the engine. He also took food, water, and blankets. He checked all of his diving equipment and made notes in a **notebook**.

A white **seagull** flew overhead as they left the harbor. Smoke bellowed from the boat's **smokestack**. Taro and Tori wore sunscreen so they wouldn't get **sunburn**.

When they reached the spot, Uncle Ken put on his diving suit and dove **underwater**. Later, he told Taro and Tori, "I didn't find any treasure, but I saw many beautiful things. A **starfish** clung to a rock and looked just like a star in the night sky. A seahorse floated in some tall, green **seaweed**. I found this beautiful striped **seashell** in the sand."

Page 59

Page 60

Name _____

Make the Connection

Word Bank

cast   port   letter   made   glasses   fall
burn   line   melon   paper   shake   light   milk
nut   wheel   book   cup   mail

Each word below is the first word of a compound word. Find words in the Word Bank that make compound words. Write the words on the lines. The first one is done for you.

news
newspaper
newscast
news letter

air
airport
airline
airmail

hand
handbook
hand made
handshake

butter
butter nut
butter cup
butter milk

sun
sunburn
sunglasses
sunlight

water
waterwheel
watermelon
waterfall

Choose one compound word from each group and use it to write a sentence.

1. answers will vary
2. _____
3. _____
4. _____
5. _____
6. _____

Use the words from your lists to answer each riddle.

1. A place where airplanes land.   airport
2. The clasping of two hands.   handshake
3. A tiny yellow flower.   buttercup
4. Reporting on the hour.   newscast
5. A picnic-lunch dessert.   watermelon
6. Skin that hurts from too much sun.   sunburn

Page 60

Page 61

Name _____

Campground Compounds

Read each compound word. On the lines write the two words that were put together to make the compound word.

1. campground	camp ground	9. bullfrog	bull frog
2. outdoors	out doors	10. waterfall	water fall
3. pinecone	pine cone	11. grasshopper	grass hopper
4. backpack	back pack	12. bedtime	bed time
5. overnight	over night	13. pancakes	pan cakes
6. firewood	fire wood	14. campfire	camp fire
7. footbridge	foot bridge	15. footpath	foot path

Read the story. Write the missing compound words on the line.

Mark and his father love the fresh air of the **outdoors**. They were excited as they planned an **overnight** camping trip. Mark put some food and trail mix in his **backpack**. Dad put juice, matches and a first-aid kit in his.

When they arrived at the **campground**, they set up camp and gathered **firewood** for a fire. Then they went hiking on the **footpath** that led to the lake. They passed a rushing **waterfall**. Mark saw a red squirrel grab a **pinecone** and race up the pine tree. A **grasshopper** hopped ahead of them on the trail. Water flowed over rocks beneath them as they crossed a small **footbridge**. When they came to the end of the trail, they watched the **sunset**.

Back at their camp, Mark and his father built a blazing **campfire**. It was so quiet that they could hear a **bullfrog** croak in the distance.

Page 61

IF87103 "Fun"damental Phonics

Page 62

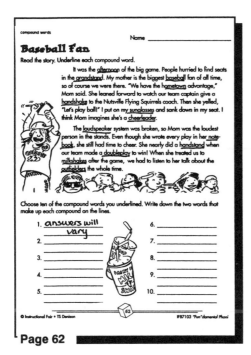

compound words

Name _____

Baseball Fan

Read the story. Underline each compound word.

It was the afternoon of the big game. People hurried to find seats in the grandstand. My mother is the biggest baseball fan of all time, so of course we were there. "We have the hometown advantage," Mom said. She leaned forward to watch our team captain give a handshake to the Nutsville Flying Squirrels coach. Then she yelled, "Let's play ball!" I put on my sunglasses and sank down in my seat. I think Mom imagines she's a cheerleader.

The loudspeaker system was broken, so Mom was the loudest person in the stands. Even though she wrote every play in her notebook, she still had time to cheer. She nearly did a handstand when our team made a doubleplay to win! When she treated us to milkshakes after the game, we had to listen to her talk about the outfielders the whole time.

Choose ten of the compound words you underlined. Write down the two words that make up each compound on the lines.

1. answers will vary
2. _____
3. _____
4. _____
5. _____
6. _____
7. _____
8. _____
9. _____
10. _____

© Instructional Fair • TS Denison   IF87103 "Fun"damental Phoni

Page 62

Page 63

compound words

Name _____

Link Up the Words

Word Bank

sun	note	play	book	head	hide
out	camp	look	suit	cook	flash
under	bed	scrap	road	take	pillow

Each word below is the second word in a compound. Find words in the Word Bank that make compound words and write the words on the lines. The first one is done for you.

book
notebook
scrap book
cook book

light
sun light
head light
flash light

ground
underground
campground
playground

side
outside
bedside
roadside

case
suitcase
book case
pillow case

out
look out
take out
hideout

Use the compound words above to answer these riddles.

1. You would want this if you were a bank robber. — hideout
2. You would want this when you were making your bed. — pillowcase
3. You would want to be here if you were a wild animal. — outside
4. You would want to be here if you were on recess. — playground
5. You would want this if your lights were out. — flashlight
6. You would want this to write in at school. — notebook
7. You would want two of these on the front of your car. — headlight
8. You would go here to set up your tent. — campground
9. You would want this to hold clothes for a trip. — suitcase
10. You would go here if you were exploring caves. — underground
11. You would need this if you had lots of books. — bookcase

Page 63

Page 64

compound words

Name _____

Till the Ground

Read the story. Draw a line under each compound word.

Farmer Jones gets up at sunrise. He has so many jobs to do! As he walks onto the porch of the farmhouse and looks around the barnyard, he can hear the chickens clucking. They are hungry!

After feeding all the animals, Farmer Jones climbs onto his tractor. He needs to plow the cornfield today. As he plows up and down the field, he thinks about how tall the cornstalks will grow and how good each ear of corn will taste. Then he plants the seeds. Knowing that the crows will want to nibble on the seeds, he stuffs an old shirt and a pair of jeans with straw. After he fastens the scarecrow to a post, he adds an old straw hat for its straw head.

The afternoon sunshine is hot, but Farmer Jones keeps working. Mrs. Jones is also busy. She has baked some homemade muffins with fresh, handpicked berries. Homegrown foods taste best to her.

At sunset, Farmer Jones and his wife sit on the porch, eating muffins and applesauce and drinking buttermilk. They smile as they watch tiny fireflies flit by the candlelight of their small lantern.

Write down ten of compound words that you underlined in the story. Then write the two words that make the compound word. answers will vary

1. sunrise / sun / rise
2. farmhouse / farm / house
3. cornfield / corn / field
4. scarecrow / scare / crow
5. homemade / home / made
6. handpicked / hand / picked
7. applesauce / apple / sauce
8. buttermilk / butter / milk
9. fireflies / fire / flies
10. candlelight / candle / light

Page 64

Page 65

contraction: /not/

Name _____

Put It Together

Write the contraction for each pair of words on the lines. Read the poems.

This soup does look good,
That soup doesn't (does not).
This soup wasn't (was not)!

Isn't (is not) this silly?
Aren't (are not) you, too?
Haven't (have not) you anything
Better to do?

Use the poems as Word Banks. Find the contraction to complete each sentence.

1. Maggie has the flu, so she isn't going on the field trip.
2. We haven't been to the new amusement park yet.
3. Saturday wasn't a good day for a picnic in the park because it rained.
4. May and David aren't excited about doing the yardwork.
5. That purple-and-green cake doesn't look very tasty!

Write a four-line poem using the contraction to start each line.
Doesn't — answers will vary
Wasn't _____
Isn't _____
Aren't _____

Page 65

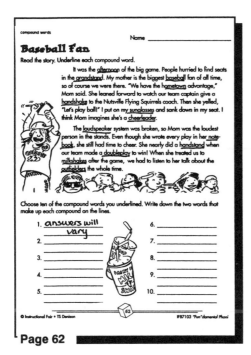

IF87103 "Fun"damental Phonics

Contract It!

contraction: /not/

Name _____

On the lines write the contraction for the two words. Read the poems.

Don't, Don't
(do not) (do not)
Okay, I won't.
(will not)

Don't do this,
(do not)
Can't do that,
(cannot)
Mustn't ever touch!
(must not)
With all the mustn'ts,
(must not)
Don'ts, and can'ts,
(do not) (cannot)
I can't do very much!
(cannot)

Use the poems as Word Banks. Find a contraction to complete each line of the poem.

My teacher says I mustn't hurry
On my way to play.

But Mom tells me I can't sleep in
Each and every day.

I don't think that I ask for much,
But this I'd like to know:

If I can't hurry out at recess,
Why won't Mom let me go slow?

Write a sentence telling about something you won't do.
answers will vary

Write a sentence telling about something you can't do.
answers will vary

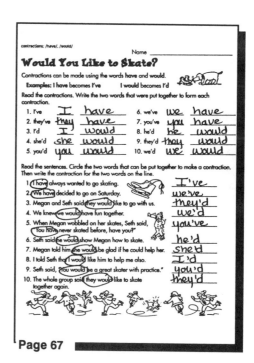

Would You Like to Skate?

contractions: /have/, /would/

Name _____

Contractions can be made using the words have and would.

Examples: I have becomes I've   I would becomes I'd

Read the contractions. Write the two words that were put together to form each contraction.

1. I've — I have
2. they've — they have
3. I'd — I would
4. she'd — she would
5. you'd — you would
6. we've — we have
7. you've — you have
8. he'd — he would
9. they'd — they would
10. we'd — we would

Read the sentences. Circle the two words that can be put together to make a contraction. Then write the contraction for the two words on the line.

1. I have always wanted to go skating. — I've
2. We have decided to go on Saturday. — we've
3. Megan and Seth said they would like to go with us. — they'd
4. We knew we would have fun together. — we'd
5. When Megan wobbled on her skates, Seth said, "You have never skated before, have you?" — you've
6. Seth said he would show Megan how to skate. — he'd
7. Megan told him she would be glad if he could help her. — she'd
8. I told Seth that I would like him to help me also. — I'd
9. Seth said, "You would be a great skater with practice." — you'd
10. The whole group said they would like to skate together again. — they'd

---

You're Where?

contractions: /are/, /am/

Name _____

Write the contraction for each two words on the lines. Read the poem.

I'm here.
(I am)
We're aware.
(we are)
You're here,
(you are)
But they're not there!
(they are)

Use the poem as a Word Bank. Find the correct contraction to finish each sentence.

1. Alesha, Shelly, and Cam say they're going ice skating.
2. I was late and now I'm going to miss the beginning of the movie!
3. Mark and I decided that we're going to write the report together.
4. You're going to like my grandmother's cottage.

On the lines write the two words that make each contraction.

we're — We are   they're — they are
I'm — I am   you're — you are

Use the contractions above to write a paragraph about a special place you would like to visit.

answers will vary

What Will You Be?

contraction: /will/

Name _____

On the line write the contraction for the two words. Read the poem.

I'll be one,
(I will)
You'll be two.
(you will)
She'll be three.
(she will)
He'll be four.
(he will)
They'll be five and six.
(they will)
Think We'll need any more?
(we will)

Read the sentences. Find the missing contraction in the poem and write it on the line.

1. Dad told us that we'll need to leave early for the airport.
2. May walks by the library, so she'll return our books for us.
3. If you forget your lunch, you'll get very hungry.
4. I have to pick up the cake, so I'll be late for the party.
5. Sara and Cole have soccer practice, so they'll need a ride home.
6. Josh said he'll meet us at the baseball field.

Use the contractions in the poem to write a poem about a game you and your friends play.

answers will vary

IF87103 "Fun"damental Phonics

What's That?

Name _____

Contractions can be made using the word **is**. Example: that is becomes that's

Read the contractions. Write the two words that were put together to form the contraction.

1. one's __one__ __is__
2. when's __when__ __is__
3. here's __here__ __is__
4. who's __who__ __is__
5. she's __she__ __is__
6. it's __it__ __is__
7. that's __that__ __is__
8. where's __where__ __is__
9. he's __he__ __is__
10. there's __there__ __is__

Read the sentences. Circle each pair of words that can make a contraction. Then write the contraction for the two words on the line.

1. When is the circus coming to town? — When's
2. Here is a poster about the circus. — Here's
3. Look it is going to be today! — It's
4. Do you know who is going? — Who's
5. Michelle says she is going with Chung. — She's
6. Clyde said he is going with his family. — He's
7. Look! There is the circus coming down the street now! — There's
8. Where is that elephant going? Oh, I see! — Where's
9. One is marching directly behind the other. — One's
10. Wow! That is the greatest parade ever! — That's

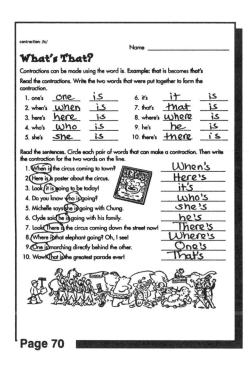

Unlike Others

Name _____

The prefix **un** means **not**. On each line, write a new word by putting **un** in front of the root word.

1. saddle __unsaddle__
2. lace __unlace__
3. clog __unclog__
4. wind __unwind__
5. pack __unpack__
6. like __unlike__
7. true __untrue__
8. stable __unstable__
9. load __unload__
10. plug __unplug__
11. able __unable__
12. lock __unlock__
13. known __unknown__
14. tie __untie__

Find the correct word from the list above to complete each sentence.

1. It is __unknown__ just how many planets we have in our universe.
2. Can you __untie__ this knot?
3. Please __unsaddle__ the horse before putting her in her stall.
4. Eva helped her mother __unload__ the groceries from the car.
5. We will use this liquid to __unclog__ the kitchen drain.
6. __unlike__ Joe to be so grumpy.
7. Mark hurt his leg and is __unable__ to run in the race Saturday.
8. Maybe this key will __unlock__ the treasure chest.
9. After the trip, Dad asked us to __unpack__ our own suitcases.
10. It is __untrue__ that the world is flat.
11. Be sure to __unplug__ the lamp before you fix the cord.
12. This rickety old ladder is too __unstable__ to climb.
13. We will have to __unwind__ this rope before we can use it.
14. Please help your little sister __unlace__ her sneakers.

Repeat It!

Name _____

The prefix **re** means **again**. On each line, write a new word by putting **re** in front of the root word.

1. lock __relock__
2. build __rebuild__
3. read __reread__
4. wrap __rewrap__
5. glue __reglue__
6. stack __restack__
7. connect __reconnect__
8. fold __refold__
9. test __retest__
10. heat __reheat__
11. appear __reappear__
12. pack __repack__
13. sew __resew__
14. copy __recopy__

Find the correct word from the list above to complete each sentence.

1. Carol's paper was so messy that she had to __recopy__ it.
2. The picture would not stay on the paper, so Pat had to __reglue__ it.
3. David ripped his shirt, so Mom will have to __resew__ it.
4. After the tornado, we had to __rebuild__ the tool shed.
5. The magic act made a lion vanish and then __reappear__ .
6. Chung helped her aunt __refold__ all the blankets.
7. The puppy knocked over the boxes, but Pete will __restack__ them.
8. Dad will __reheat__ the cold soup.
9. Mrs. Ramirez said she would __rewrap__ the package.
10. It took two hours before they could __reconnect__ the power.
11. Sara had to __repack__ her suitcase to get everything in it.
12. "Please __reread__ the story," said Mrs. Patten.

Impossible!

Name _____

The prefixes **in**, **im**, and **ir** all mean **not**. Read the words. Draw a line under the prefix of each word.

impossible   informal   immobile
impatient   irregular   irresponsible
inactive   irresistible   invisible
improper   inaccurate   imperfect

Use the list as a Word Bank. Find the correct word to complete each sentence.

1. It is __impossible__ even for a weightlifter to lift a ton.
2. The chipped handle made the pitcher __imperfect__ .
3. The computer is __inactive__ because the software isn't loaded yet.
4. Megan was __irresponsible__ when she left her coat on the playground.
5. Screaming in a library is __improper__ behavior.
6. The picnic will be __informal__ , so feel free to wear shorts or jeans.
7. The smell of fresh-baked cookies is __irresistible__ .
8. Sara was so __impatient__ that she stormed out of the house without her brother.
9. The doctor was worried about her __irregular__ heartbeat.
10. It is __inaccurate__ to say that everyone likes chocolate ice cream.
11. Four flat tires will make a car __immobile__ .
12. A thick fog made the boat __invisible__ to those on shore.

IF87103 "Fun"damental Phonics

Don't Disappear!

Name _____

The prefix dis means not or opposite of. On each line, write a new word by putting dis in front of the root word.

1. appear — disappear
2. honest — dishonest
3. trust — distrust
4. connect — disconnect
5. obey — disobey
6. like — dislike
7. pleased — displeased
8. courage — discourage
9. respect — disrespect
10. approve — disapprove
11. believed — disbelieved
12. comfort — discomfort

Find the correct word from the list above to complete each sentence.

1. Pete's broken ankle caused him some discomfort.
2. It is dishonest to take something that does not belong to you.
3. Sara must really dislike vegetables.
4. How did the magician make the rabbits disappear?
5. You should not show disrespect to those in authority.
6. The repairman had to disconnect the cable from the television set.
7. I distrust that character in the mystery I'm reading; I think he's lying.
8. I disapprove of your plan to go to the mall by yourself.
9. Dad was very displeased that our puppy shredded his shirt.
10. The librarian will discourage people from talking in the library.
11. Why did Dan disobey Mom and go fishing without permission?
12. My teacher disbelieved my story that the dog ate my homework.

Page 74

Follow the Signs

Name _____

When you add the suffix s to a noun, it changes it to mean more than one.

1. cabin — cabins
2. guest — guests
3. table — tables
4. balloon — balloons
5. map — maps
6. firework — fireworks
7. car — cars
8. can — cans
9. invitation — invitations
10. hamburger — hamburgers

Find the correct words from the list above to complete the letter.

Dear Becky,

Mia and I had so much fun this weekend! She invited some of her friends to stay in her family's guest cabins for two days. We mailed invitations to everyone last week. On Saturday, everyone loaded their cars to start the trip to the lake. Mia and I had marked maps to show the right roads to take.

At the end of the driveway, Mia and I had tied a big bunch of red balloons to a tree. Nobody had trouble finding the right place to turn! By noon, all of Mia's guests were here.

Uncle Joe cooked hamburgers, and Mia and I handed out cans of juice to everybody. We sat at big, round tables under the pine trees. When it was dark, we walked down to the lake to watch the fireworks display. We had a wonderful holiday.

Love,
Eva

Page 75

Flashes and Crashes

Name _____

To make a word plural when it ends in the letter s, ss, x, ch, or sh, you must add the suffix es. Write the plural of each word. Read the words out loud.

1. patch — patches
2. wish — wishes
3. crash — crashes
4. glass — glasses
5. coach — coaches
6. brush — brushes
7. box — boxes
8. flash — flashes
9. stitch — stitches
10. bench — benches

Find the correct word, singular or plural, from the list above to complete each sentence.

1. Both coaches talked to their teams before the game started.
2. Brad carried out two boxes filled with mitts and baseballs.
3. Then he used a brush to sweep the dirt off the bases.
4. Steve's uniform had a tear, so his mom sewed a patch over it.
5. Both teams talked about their wishes to win the game.
6. Coach Green did not think Sara's cut would need any stitches.
7. Suddenly there were flashes of lightning across the sky.
8. Then there were loud crashes of thunder.
9. All the players ran to the dugouts and sat on the benches.
10. One of the snack bars sent free glasses of lemonade to the players.

Read the words. Write a sentence using each of the words.

matches   dresses   brushes   switches

1. answers will vary
2. _____
3. _____
4. _____

Page 76

Picked and Packed

Name _____

The suffix ed changes a verb so it tells something that happened in the past. This suffix has three possible sounds: "d" as in called, "t" as in helped, and "ed" as in added.

Read the words. Draw a line under the suffix ed. Then write each word under the sound that the ed makes in that word.

Word Bank

turned	opened	planted	watched
listed	cleaned	talked	needed
packed	boasted	spelled	laughed

ed		
listed	turned	packed
boasted	opened	talked
planted	cleaned	watched
needed	spelled	laughed

Use the list above as a Word Bank. Select the correct word that rhymes with the underlined word to finish the poem.

When fall came, the apples were packed.
The week before hay was racked.

We worked every day 'till the wheat was gleaned.
The chimneys were swept and the barn was cleaned.

After that, we made plans and talked.
As over the fields we rode and walked.

And as the leaves to scarlet turned,
We saw to it that a bonfire burned.

By that fire we told tales and boasted,
With cider mulling and chestnuts roasted.

Page 77

IF87103 "Fun"damental Phonics

Page 78

suffix: /ing/

Name _____

Spring Cleaning

Read the words. On the line write the word and add the suffix ing.

1. clean — cleaning
2. plant — planting
3. carry — carrying
4. dust — dusting
5. add — adding
6. look — looking
7. vacuum — vacuuming
8. rain — raining
9. wash — washing
10. lift — lifting

Read the sentences. Find the missing word that will correctly complete each sentence and write it on the line.

1. It's spring and time for planting vegetable and flower gardens.
2. As soon as everyone goes outside, it starts raining.
3. Mom says it's a good time for cleaning the house.
4. Sharon grabs a rag and starts dusting the furniture.
5. Greg begins vacuuming the carpets.
6. Mike starts washing the windows.
7. Harriet is looking in the closet for toys she no longer wants.
8. She is small and has trouble lifting the heavy box.
9. Sharon helps her by carrying the box downstairs.
10. Just when we thought we were finished, we saw Mom adding more jobs to the list!

Read the words. Write a tongue-twister using each of the words

staying   showing   painting

1. answers will vary
2. _____
3. _____

Page 78

Page 79

suffix: /ly/

Name _____

Read Silently, Please!

The suffix ly means in a certain way or having the quality or characteristics of. Read the words. On the line, write the word and add the suffix ly.

1. great — greatly
2. foolish — foolishly
3. usual — usually
4. quick — quickly
5. brave — bravely
6. friend — friendly
7. direct — directly
8. wise — wisely
9. quiet — quietly

Read the story. Use the list above as a Word Bank. Find the correct words to complete the story.

Our librarian, Ms. Ray, is friendly and helps everyone. We know we must work quietly while in the library. Our class usually goes to the library every Tuesday. On one visit, George acted foolishly and ended up knocking a stack of books onto the floor. When Ms. Ray asked who was responsible, George bravely admitted it was his fault. He apologized and quickly picked up all of the books. He promised Ms. Ray he would act wisely in the future. Ms. Ray told George that she greatly appreciated his honesty. After the library time, George walked directly back to our classroom.

Read the words. Write a sentence using each of the words.

tightly   strongly   gladly   timely   really

1. answers will vary
2. _____
3. _____
4. _____
5. _____

Page 79

Page 80

suffixes: /er/, /or/

Name _____

Be a Word Inventor!

The suffixes er and or mean a person who does something. Underline the suffix in each word.

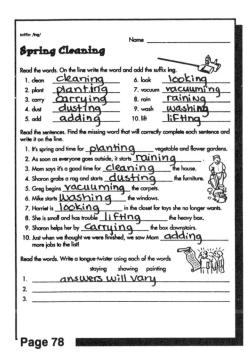

Word Bank

actor, farmer, painter, inventor, printer, baker, miner, singer, helper, plumber, teacher, miner

Read the riddles. Find the answer in the Word Bank and write it on the line.

1. This person is to a classroom as a captain is to a ship. teacher
2. This person creates a different life on the stage. actor
3. This person pans for gold! miner
4. This person can change the color of your whole house. painter
5. This person's job is down the drain! plumber
6. This person puts words and pictures on paper. printer
7. This person grows the food we eat. farmer
8. This person needs to get up early to knead! baker
9. This person has a musical voice. singer
10. This person figures out new ways to get things done. inventor

Choose three words from the Word Bank. Write a sentence using each of these words.

1. answers will vary
2. _____
3. _____

Page 80

Page 81

suffixes: /able/

Name _____

Are You Able?

The suffix able means can be done. On each line, write the word and add the suffix able. Read the words out loud.

1. wash — washable
2. enjoy — enjoyable
3. break — breakable
4. beat — beatable
5. like — likeable
6. move — moveable
7. reason — reasonable
8. change — changeable
9. train — trainable
10. comfort — comfortable

Use the list above as a Word Bank. Find the correct word to complete each sentence.

1. Old jeans are soft and comfortable.
2. Sheets and towels are washable.
3. Something fun is enjoyable.
4. Something made of glass could be breakable.
5. A friendly person is likeable.
6. Something you can lift and move is moveable.
7. A puppy can be taught, so he's trainable.
8. A team that can be beaten is beatable.
9. Something that changes often is changeable.
10. Something that makes sense is reasonable.

Add able to these words: depend, like, and agree. Write a description of someone who has all three of these traits.

answers will vary
_____
_____

Page 81

125

© Instructional Fair • TS Denison

IF87103 "Fun"damental Phonics

Get to the Root

A root word is a base word to which prefixes and/or suffixes can be added. A root word is a word all by itself. In the word unwashed, the root word is wash.

Read each word. Find the root word and write it on the line.

1. impossible __im-possible__
2. unimportant __un-important__
3. dishonest __dis-honest__
4. discovered __dis-cover-ed__
5. reaction __re-action__
6. disagreeable __dis-agree-able__
7. unkindly __un-kind-ly__
8. reconstructed __re-construct-ed__
9. misplace __mis-place__
10. planted __plant-ed__

11. cleanable __clean-able__
12. cleaning __clean-ing__
13. directly __direct-ly__
14. disobeyed __dis-obey-ed__
15. unlocks __un-locks__
16. redoing __re-doing__
17. visitor __visit-or__
18. visiting __visit-ing__
19. uncomfortable __un-comfort-able__
20. builder __build-er__

★ Rather than total syllabication, look for root words.
Here's a prefix-suffix machine! Put the root word in and add the prefix and suffix. Write the new word on the line.

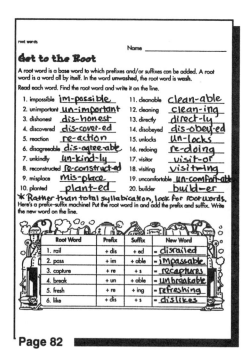

Root Word	Prefix	Suffix	New Word
1. rail	+ dis	+ ed	= disrailed
2. pass	+ im	+ able	= impassable
3. capture	+ re	+ s	= recaptures
4. break	+ un	+ able	= unbreakable
5. fresh	+ re	+ ing	= refreshing
6. like	+ dis	+ s	= dislikes

Divide at the Root

Prefixes and suffixes are syllables by themselves. Syllables are chunks of words. Read the words. On the line write the words in syllables. Draw a straight line (—) to show where they are divided. The first one is done for you.

1. mislead __mis-lead__
2. talking __talk-ing__
3. rewrite __re-write__
4. dislike __dis-like__
5. comfortable __comfort-able__

6. unmade __un-made__
7. teacher __teach-er__
8. distrust __dis-trust__
9. ordering __order-ing__
10. gladly __glad-ly__

Use the words above as a Word Bank. Find the correct word to answer each riddle.

1. Doing this in class is not always allowed. __talking__
2. This is another word for "happily." __gladly__
3. This is the opposite of "like." __dislike__
4. When you don't pull up the sheets and blankets on your bed, it's this. __unmade__
5. This is when you were led to the wrong place or idea. __mislead__
6. This is when you have to do a story over again. __rewrite__
7. This word describes something soft and cozy. __comfortable__
8. This is the person who explains things in class. __teacher__
9. This is when you tell a waiter what you would like to eat. __ordering__
10. This is when you don't trust someone. __distrust__

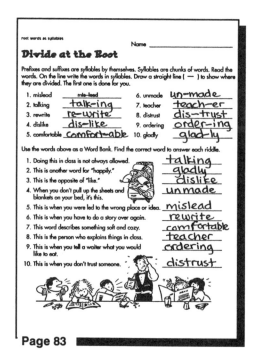

Pair of Pears

A homophone is a word that sounds just like another word, but it is spelled differently and has a different meaning. Read the poem out loud.

That pear and that pear,
That pair over there,
That pair of pears
Are they their pears?
No, they're ours!

Read the clues. Find the correct homophone in the poem and write it on the line.

1. This word is a contraction. __they're__
2. It is one of a pair. __pear__
3. Where our pair of pears are located. __there__
4. This is what two pears are called. __pair__

Read the sentences. Find the missing word in the Word Bank and write it on the line.

Word Bank: tea, tee, plane, plain, soar, sore, shoo, shoe

1. Diana likes the __plain__ dress better than the frilly one.
2. Paula told the cat to __shoo__ out of her garden.
3. Watch that hawk __soar__ toward the treetop.
4. Aunt May likes a cup of hot __tea__ on a cold day.
5. Mom places the golf ball on a __tee__ before she swings her club.
6. Jeff found his other __shoe__ under the couch.
7. Our __plane__ landed smoothly on the runway.
8. The splinter made my finger __sore__.

That Makes Sense

Read the poem. Circle the homophones.

I was sent a whole cent
That I knew wasn't new.
The whole thing had a hole
I thought, "What can I buy
With a cent with a hole?
No, I know! A doughnut hole!"

Read the clues. Find the missing homophone in the poem and write it in the puzzle.

Across:
1. The boy in the poem _____ his cent wasn't new.
5. This was in the center of his cent.
6. The opposite of "yes."
7. The opposite of "old."

Down:
1. The homophone of no.
2. This word means "all of something."
3. The homophone of cent.
4. This means "one penny."

Crossword:
knew, whole, cent, no, new, hole, not, sent

Find the correct word in the Word Bank to complete each sentence.

Word Bank: peek, peak, heard, herd, by, buy

1. My little brother tried to __peek__ at his birthday presents before the party.
2. Jonathan helps his dad __herd__ the cattle to the new range.
3. They need to __buy__ tickets for the concert.
4. Mount McKinley is the highest mountain __peak__ in North America.
5. She walked __by__ the bookstore on her way to school.
6. We __heard__ an owl hooting late at night.

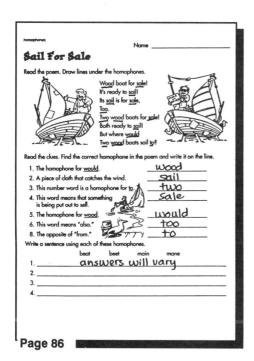

Sail For Sale

Read the poem. Draw lines under the homophones.

Wood boat for sale!
It's ready to sail!
Its sail is for sale,
Too.
Two wood boats for sale!
Both ready to sail
But where would
Two wood boats sail to?

Read the clues. Find the correct homophone in the poem and write it on the line.

1. The homophone for would. — wood
2. A piece of cloth that catches the wind. — sail
3. This number word is a homophone for to. — two
4. This word means that something is being put out to sell. — sale
5. The homophone for wood. — would
6. This word means "also." — too
7. —
8. The opposite of "from." — to

Write a sentence using each of these homophones.

beat   beet   main   mane

1. answers will vary
2. _____
3. _____
4. _____

Page 86

Hoarse Horse

Read the poem. Draw lines under the homophones.

My horse was hoarse
And weak all week.
As we rode on the road,
He could hardly speak!
He sighed by my side.
As bored as a board.
But when I fed him hay,
Hey, his spirit soared!

Read the clues. Find the correct homophone in the poem and write it on the line.

1. He was hoarse and weak all week. — horse
2. My hoarse horse and I rode on this. — road
3. My horse was hoarse and felt weak for this long. — week
4. My hoarse horse sighed as he stood here. — side
5. My horse had this medical problem. — hoarse
6. My hoarse horse looked like this as he sighed by my side. — bored
7. I fed this to my hoarse horse. — hay
8. This is what I said when my hoarse horse's spirit soared! — hey
9. My hoarse horse felt like this all week. — weak
10. My hoarse horse and I did this on a road. — rode
11. My hoarse horse looked as bored as this as he sighed by my side. — board

Page 87

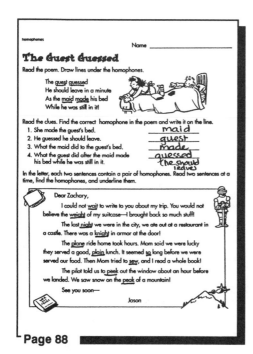

The Guest Guessed

Read the poem. Draw lines under the homophones.

The guest guessed
He should leave in a minute
As the maid made his bed
While he was still in it!

Read the clues. Find the correct homophone in the poem and write it on the line.

1. She made the guest's bed. — maid
2. He guessed he should leave. — guest
3. What the maid did to the guest's bed. — made
4. What the guest did after the maid made his bed while he was still in it. — guessed he should leave

In the letter, each two sentences contain a pair of homophones. Read two sentences at a time, find the homophones, and underline them.

Dear Zachary,

I could not wait to write to you about my trip. You would not believe the weight of my suitcase—I brought back so much stuff!

The last night we were in the city, we ate out at a restaurant in a castle. There was a knight in armor at the door!

The plane ride home took hours. Mom said we were lucky they served a good, plain lunch. It seemed so long before we were served our food. Then Mom tried to sew, and I read a whole book!

The pilot told us to peek out the window about an hour before we landed. We saw snow on the peak of a mountain!

See you soon—

Jason

Page 88

One Lead to Another

Read the poem. Circle the homophones.

Two tall pencils had a race.
The first led by its lead
But the second passed past
Erasing very fast.
The second one won by a head!

Read the sentences. Find the correct homophone in the poem and write it on the line.

1. My brother's team __won__ every game last season.
2. Our bus __passed__ by the new building site.
3. Chung read a book about Korea's __past__.
4. Which __one__ of these shirts do you like?
5. Beth's pencil __lead__ broke in the middle of the test.
6. Gordon __led__ the rest of the sprinters and won the race.

Read the poem. The homophones are mixed up! In the space with the numbers, write the correct homophone for each word.

In you're library
your not aloud
To talk allowed.
And if books are late,
You'll fined
You will be find!

1. your
2. you're
3. allowed
4. aloud
5. find
6. fined

Page 89

　　　IF87103 "Fun"damental Phonics

homophones

I Read in Bed

Name _____

Read the poem. Draw lines under the homophones.

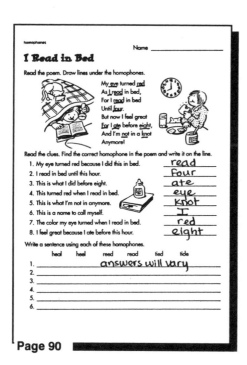

My eye turned red
As I read in bed,
For I read in bed
Until four.
But now I feel great
For I ate before eight,
And I'm not in a knot
Anymore!

Read the clues. Find the correct homophone in the poem and write it on the line.

1. My eye turned red because I did this in bed. **read**
2. I read in bed until this hour. **Four**
3. This is what I did before eight. **ate**
4. This turned red when I read in bed. **eye**
5. This is what I'm not in anymore. **knot**
6. This is a name to call myself. **I**
7. The color my eye turned when I read in bed. **red**
8. I feel great because I ate before this hour. **eight**

Write a sentence using each of these homophones.

heal   heel   reed   read   tied   tide

1. _____ answers will vary _____
2. _____
3. _____
4. _____
5. _____
6. _____

Page 90

---

homophones

An Ant and His Aunt

Name _____

Read the poem. Circle the homophones.

An ant and his aunt
stare at the stair.
The son sighs at the size.
The sun says, "It's time!
It's our hour to climb.
Let's do it before the dew dries."

Use the homophones from the poem above to complete the poem below. Each pair of lines contains one pair of homophones.

When we go on a picnic, my Aunt May **sighs**
At the **size** of our huge family!

She moans, "People will **stare** as we walk down the **stair** s,
As we start off so happily."

Then, when **Aunt** May finds a place to serve lunch,
She screams at the sight of black **ant** s.

She says, "The **hour** has come to start all **our** fun,
So you must go back to the plants!"

Late in the day, our darling Aunt May hates to find the grass wet with **dew**
She says, "Let's do go home; please, let's **do** !

The grass is too damp for our huge family camp,
But it was lovely to be here with you!"

Page 91

---

homophones

The Hair of a Hare

Name _____

Read the poem. Circle the homophones. On the lines below the poem, write the pairs of homophones.

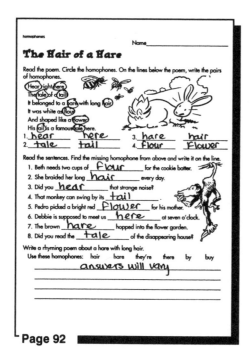

Hear right here
The tale of a tail
It belonged to a hare with long hair
It was white as flour
And shaped like a flower
His tail is a famous tale here.

1. **hear** **here**   3. **hare** **hair**
2. **tale** **tail**   4. **flour** **Flower**

Read the sentences. Find the missing homophone from above and write it on the line.

1. Beth needs two cups of **flour** for the cookie batter.
2. She braided her long **hair** every day.
3. Did you **hear** that strange noise?
4. That monkey can swing by its **tail** .
5. Pedro picked a bright red **flower** for his mother.
6. Debbie is supposed to meet us **here** at seven o'clock.
7. The brown **hare** hopped into the flower garden.
8. Did you read the **tale** of the disappearing house?

Write a rhyming poem about a hare with long hair.
Use these homophones: hair hare they're there by buy

_____ answers will vary _____
_____
_____
_____

Page 92

---

homophones

Homing in on Homophones

Name _____

Read the poem. Draw a line under the homophones.

Each flower in those rows
Is a rose, I suppose.
How do I know?
My nose knows!

Read the clues. Find the correct homophone in the poem and write it on the line.

1. The roses are planted in these. **rows**
2. My face has two eyes, a mouth, and this. **nose**
3. The homophone for nose. **knows**
4. This is a type of flower. **rose**

Read the clues. Find the missing word in the Word Bank and write it in the puzzle.

Word Bank: bear blew roll seam wrap
bare blue role seem rap

Across:
1. Max will play the ____ of a knight in the play.
2. Sara will sew up that torn ____ .
3. We have to paint the sky ____ .
4. A big brown ____ walked out of the cave.
5. I need some paper to ____ Mom's present.

Down:
1. This ____ was baked today.
2. It doesn't ____ very hot outside.
3. The tree looks ____ without leaves.
4. The wind ____ dust everywhere.
6. Did the mail carrier ____ on the door?

Page 93

© Instructional Fair • TS Denison

IF87103 "Fun"damental Phonics